MICE
AND RATS

Joyce Lawrence

HAMLYN

Published 1986 by Hamlyn Publishing,
Bridge House, London Road, Twickenham, Middlesex

Copyright © Hamlyn Publishing 1986
a division of The Hamlyn Publishing Group Ltd

ISBN 0 600 30734 4
Printed in Italy

Some of the illustrations in this book are reproduced from other books
published by The Hamlyn Publishing Group Ltd

Contents

Introduction

Both mice and rats that are kept as pets have originated from the wild forms which are thought of by many people as pests and carriers of disease. The pet mouse is descended from the House Mouse (*Mus musculus*) and the rat from the Common Brown Rat (*Rattus norvegicus*). Both are rodents belonging to the family Muridae. The distinguishing features of this group are a long relatively hairless tail and constantly growing incisor teeth to facilitate gnawing. Mice measure approximately 8 cm (3 in) in length, with a tail of similar size. Rats are larger, being at least 25 cm (10 in) long, again with a tail of similar length. As a group they are easily tamed and can become very responsive if handled regularly. Fully tamed individuals hardly ever bite.

While rats are active throughout the day there is a tendency for mice to be nocturnal. If properly looked after and cleaned out regularly they are not as smelly as is often claimed. It is usually accepted that females are relatively odourless compared with males, the males' odour being associated with scent marking of its territory.

Mice live for no more than one to two years, with exceptional individuals living as long as three years. Rats live slightly longer, up to three or four years. Mice and rats have been widely bred for use as laboratory animals, most of these animals being white in colour. However, mice and rats have been selectively bred to develop over 40 varieties of mice, and more than 30 of rats.

Mice (top) and rats (bottom) make extremely interesting and attractive pets.

Choosing and Buying

There are many varieties of mouse and rat to choose from, with variations both in coat colour and texture. Purchasing from pet shops will provide you with good specimens but a limited choice of varieties. For a wider selection the best source is the hobby breeder. Before buying, however, you would be best advised to visit shows to see the varieties being exhibited. This will also give you the opportunity to develop an 'eye' for the strong healthy animal as well as meeting the local breeders.

When purchasing new stock choose immature animals. Mice should be between five and six weeks old and rats between four and five weeks, these younger animals being more easily and quickly tamed. When purchasing mice and rats a number of points should be checked and the animals examined using the following list as a guide.

Signs of health
Head
Nose Clean, no discharge.
Eyes Clear and bright, no discharge.
Ears Clean, no waxy discharge or scabs.
Teeth Growing straight and parallel, not overlong.
Head Held level.
Body
Coat Should be sleek and smooth with no bare patches, scabs, sores or wounds.
Claws None missing or damaged.
Anus Check for soiling. Staining could mean diarrhoea.

6

Legs No symptoms of paralysis or weakness; should move freely.

Weight Should not be over fat or too skinny. Overweight animals, especially if skin lumps are present, are usually at least one year old.

Daytime drowsiness is, of course, normal in mice as they are nocturnal. However, you should not buy rats that are sleepy or hiding in the corner of the cage. Rats should only be purchased if they are alert and inquisitive, but not aggressive. Faeces in the cage should be well formed and dark brown in colour.

Unless you are going to breed, males and females should not be kept together. If you want to keep more than one animal in a single cage, females are preferable as they will not fight. If breeding is to be undertaken, purchase a trio of animals made up of two females and one male.

While most mice kept in Britain are derived from the common House Mouse, other species are occasionally offered as pets. These include the Deer Mouse (*Peromyscus leucopus*), Dormice – Common (*Muscardinus ovellanarius*) and Edible (*Glis glis*), Harvest Mouse (*Micromys minutus*), Wood Mouse (*Apodemus sylvaticus*), and the Yellow-Necked Mouse (*Apodemus flavicollis*). The only other species of rat that is occasionally offered as a pet is the Kangaroo Rat (*Dipodomys desertii*). They can all be maintained under similar conditions to those described in this book. The one exception is the Dormouse which will hibernate during the winter unless maintained at a steady temperature between 20 and 25°C (68–77°F).

Breeds and Colours

Mice

All adult mice are about the same size but there are many colour variations available.

Self-Coloured

These mice are all one colour, including the skin, ears, nose, tail and belly. Colours include Black, Blue, Champagne, Chocolate, Cream, Dove, Fawn, Red, Silver and White. They all have either pink or black eyes.

Natural-coloured Mouse

Black and White Short-haired Mouse

Silver Tan Mouse

Tan Brown Mouse

Tans
These come in the same colours as the self-coloured (above) varieties but they have golden feet and belly.

Marked
These are much more distinctive with a wide variety of patterns and colours.
Dutch Contrasting coloured patches on the face, eyes and ears, but not under the jaw. They have saddle markings from the tail to the middle of the body. Black or pink eyes.
Evens Any recognized colour with spots or patches of a contrasting colour with pink or black eyes.

9

Brokens These have many more patches or spots than the previous two varieties: they must have a spot or patch on the side of the nose, with pink or black eyes.

Variegated Any colour with splashes of a contrasting colour, pink or black eyes.

Himalayan White coat with coloured nose, feet, ears and tail, red or black eyes.

Chinchillas Pearl grey coat, black tips to hairs and slate blue undercolour, white belly and black eyes.

Silver Fox Blue, chocolate or black with a white belly and white ticking (coloured tip of hair) on sides and rump. Black eyes.

Seal Point Siamese Beige body, seal points (chestnut tipped hairs) on ears, feet, tail and muzzle.

Rump White Any colour with white rump, hind feet and tail.

Tri-colour Three patches of colour on the back and sides.

Coats

Astrex Curly coat; any colour with curly whiskers.

Long-haired Long silky coat of any recognized colour.

Satins These have a coat of any colour with a satin-like gloss to it.

Other Varieties

Agouti or Silver Agouti Brown, golden or silver body and feet with black ticking, golden belly and black eyes.

Cinnamons Golden tan, dark brown ticking with black eyes.

Sables Dark brown on back, shading to a golden belly.

Pearls Pale silver paling to whitish undercolour. The hairs are tipped with grey or black. Black eyes.

10

Argentes Silver and fawn coat with blue undercolour and pink eyes.

Argente Cream Cream and silver coat with pale blue undercolour, white belly and pink eyes.

Silver Grey Recognized in three colours: dark, medium and light. Undercolour blue-black and black eyes.

Silver Brown Undercolour deep chestnut, black eyes.

Silver Fawn Undercolour bright orange, black or pink eyes.

Sables Rich dark brown colour on back paling to rich golden tan on belly.

Marten Sables Dark sepia top coat paling on flanks. White belly with black eyes.

Rats

Colour

Agouti Rich brown with dark grey undercolour and silver belly, black guard hairs (outer-layer hairs) and black eyes.

Cinnamon Russet brown with grey undercolour and light silver belly, dark brown guard hairs and black eyes.

Silver Fawn Orange fawn with a white belly, silver guard hairs and red eyes.

Pearl Pale silver with cream undercolour and silver grey belly, grey tipped guard hairs and black eyes.

Cinnamon Pearl Banded colours – cream, blue, orange; silver grey belly, silver guard hairs, black eyes.

Black Completely black with black eyes.

Mink Completely beige with red eyes.

Pink-eyed White Completely white with pink eyes.

Siamese Beige body darkening towards the tail with light beige belly, dark points and ruby eyes.

Cream Long-haired Mouse

Black and White Long-haired Mouse

Himalayan White body with dark sepia points and red eyes.

Pattern
Hooded White body with a coloured hood. The hood involves the head, throat and shoulder areas with the saddle running down the spine to the tail. The edges of the hood and saddle must be distinct.
Berkshire Any recognized body colour with a white chest and belly. White on the limbs and tail with a white spot on the forehead.
Irish Any recognized body colour with a white equilateral triangle on the chest, the broad end in

between the forelegs. The fore-feet should be all white.
Capped Body colour white with a cap of a recognized colour variety. The colour should follow the line of the jaw but not extend past the ears or involve the chin. A white spot or blaze must be present on the face.
Variegated The head and shoulders should be of a recognized colour. The belly and the blaze on the face should be white. Variegations to cover the remainder of the body.
Silvered The coat can be of any recognized colour but it must contain an equal number of silvered and non-silvered hairs; a coloured tip is allowed.

Coat
Rex Any recognized colour but the coat to be dense and curly.

White Rat

Brown Rat

13

Housing

A variety of housing is available for mice and rats, including wooden, plastic or metal cages available from pet shops. Glass aquaria are also suitable to which a secure lid can be attached. The bars in a cage should be set close together to prevent escape, not less than 6 mm (0.25 in) apart. As both mice and rats are rodents they will try to gnaw their way out of cages. Soft wood therefore should not be used in cage construction and all exposed edges should be metal bound. Whilst the maxim 'the larger the cage the better' should be followed, minimum requirements for floor area per animal in a cage are as follows:

Mice: 30 × 30 cm (1 × 1 ft) per animal.

Rats: 60 × 60 cm (2 × 2 ft) per animal.

A cage measuring 46 × 25 × 23 cm (18 × 10 × 9 in) is suitable accommodation for two mice or one rat. If a breeding trio of mice is to be kept, the cage should measure 61 × 38 × 25 cm (24 × 15 × 9 in).

The cages should be situated out of direct sunlight in a dry, well-ventilated room at a temperature between 20 and 25°C (68–77°F). They cannot be kept outside in northern latitudes, except during the summer, but even then they are at risk from prowling cats.

Accessories

The bottom of the cage should be covered with sawdust or wood shavings, peat or sand, to a depth of 5 cm (2 in). To reduce smells originating in the cage, cat litter has been recommended as a substrate. If it is used it should be put on the bottom of the cage under the sawdust, etc. Hay and shredded paper can be used for bedding in a separate nest box which should be situated off the floor of the cage with a ladder for access. The access hole in a mouse nesting box should be no larger than 4 cm (1.5 in) in diameter.

Mice and rats usually use one place in the cage for a toilet. This area should be cleaned daily to prevent the cage smelling unpleasant. Throughout the rest of the cage, the sawdust should be changed twice a week and the cage thoroughly scrubbed out and disinfected once a month. Particular attention should be paid to the corners of the cage at every cleaning. The bedding should be replaced twice a week, a small amount of old bedding being returned with the new to retain the familiar smell.

Easily cleaned earthenware food and water bowls of a non-tip design can be provided but water bottles with nipple drinkers and hopper-type feed dispensers are preferable. Drinking bottles and food containers should be washed with soapy water daily. They must not be washed in the same bowl as household utensils nor should they be allowed to share the draining board.

With such active animals the provision of a variety of cage furniture is recommended. Mice may spend many hours in an exercise wheel and will probably run miles in a day. Never use spoked wheels as the long tail may get caught and always purchase exercise wheels with a solid back. Ladders and branches can be placed in the cage for climbing into the nest box. Do not purchase any cage accessories which have sharp edges. Wooden objects and twigs can also be provided for the animals to chew on, for example pieces of soft wood, branches of apple,

An ordinary cage (above) suitable for mice, and some playthings (right). Rats must be provided with larger cages and intricate play runs.

blackthorn and willow, cotton reels, nuts and proprietary rodent chews. They will keep the animal's teeth in good condition and perhaps prevent it from gnawing the cage. Lengths of plastic or earthenware pipe and cardboard tubing will act as artificial burrows.

Handling

When young, mice and rats can be quite nervous and easily frightened. Mishandling at this stage can affect their behaviour towards the owner in the future. Initially cage cleaning and handling should be done quietly and with as little fuss as possible. After a few days, when they will have settled into their new environment, you can put your hand in to allow them to get used to your smell and presence.

The next stage is to offer titbits in your fingers, allowing the animal to investigate the palm of your hand. Mice can be encouraged to sit in your cupped hands to be picked up; they are reluctant jumpers and therefore are

Never hold a mouse by the tail without supporting the body on the palm of the hand.

unlikely to leap to freedom. Rats are significantly larger so they can be picked up by placing one hand over the rat's back, with its nose towards your wrist, the fingers are then closed around its belly and as the animal is lifted, your other hand passes under the rat to support it. Alternatively, a rat can be picked up by placing a hand around the shoulders and if a close examination of the animal is to be undertaken the thumb can be repositioned under the lower jaw to prevent biting. It is essential to hold the animal firmly, but without squeezing so tightly that you make it difficult for it to breathe. Never pick up rats by the tail or the scruff of the neck – they will bite!

When picking up a mouse, use the base of the tail, prior to placing it on the palm of your hand. Time taken to develop a caring and trusting relationship with the individual in your charge will be rewarded.

Two of the ways to handle a rat correctly.

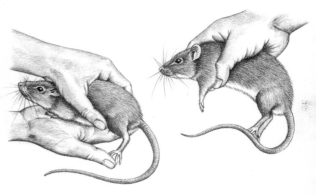

Feeding

Proprietary brands of food can be purchased from most pet shops. They are usually cereal-based containing barley, maize and rolled oats. Additional foods can be given to augment this basic diet. They include toasted wholemeal bread, peanuts, millet, dog meal and dog biscuits. Washed green foods such as grass, dandelion, chickweed, clover, coltsfoot, comfrey, dock, groundsel, vetch, cauliflower leaves and sprouts are also recommended, along with other fruits and vegetables such as apples, carrots, bananas, pears, turnips, spinach, watercress, peas (cooked and uncooked) and tomatoes. Protein in the form of dog and cat food, hamburger, bacon, hard boiled eggs and meal worms can also be offered as a treat.

Mice will eat about 7 g (0.25 oz) of the basic diet each day with rats taking up to 42 g (1.5 oz). Green foods, fruit and vegetables should only be offered two or three times a week. Uneaten food should be removed from the cage daily to prevent it going stale; this includes stores of food which may be hidden in the bedding. No vitamin or mineral supplements should be necessary if a balanced diet is being provided. Try to feed your pet at the same time each day; they will get to know the routine and will wait expectantly for you.

Do *not* feed mice with cheese; it has been associated with digestive upsets. Green food must be well washed and dried before use and only small quantities should be offered at a time. No plants should be offered to your pet which are likely to have been sprayed with pesticide or that have been collected from the roadside because of lead contamination from exhaust fumes.

Water should always be available in a non-tip container or preferably a gravity-fed bottle, which avoids contamination of the water with food and faeces.

Rats can drink quite large quantities of water each day, therefore either provide two bottles or check the water level at least twice daily. Water should be changed daily with the bottle being sterilized at least twice a week. Small quantities of milk are enjoyed by both mice and rats. However, if it is not drunk immediately milk should be removed from the cage to prevent it going sour. Milk is particularly valuable to pregnant females.

Mice need some green foodstuffs in their diet: clover (left) and dandelion (right) are both acceptable.

Breeding

Sexing

Sexing is difficult in mice until they are about ten days old. The distinguishing feature used to sex both mice and rats is the relative position of the anus and the genital opening. In the male the distance between the anus and the penis is only about half the distance between the anus and the vulva in the female. Comparing the two sexes from about a month of age should provide few problems to even the most inexperienced eye. In adult mice the area between the anus and the vulva is hairless, making sexing particularly easy. The same distinguishing features can be used to sex rats.

Mating

Mice are sexually mature at about six to seven weeks of age although breeding should not start until the buck is ten weeks old and the doe 12 weeks. The rat becomes sexually mature some two to three weeks later than the

Sexing rats and mice

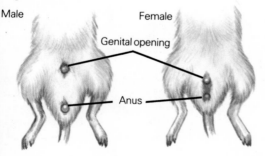

Male   Female

Genital opening

Anus

mouse but ideally should not be used for breeding until it is three to ten months old.

Both rats and mice come on heat every four or five days, with the heat lasting approximately 14 hours. The male will sniff the hind end of the female and if receptive she will raise her rump moving the tail to the side. Mating takes place very quickly lasting at most two to three seconds but this will be repeated several times.

For selective breeding it is best to use a trio of one male and two females. You will need four cages, one to house the male, one for the two females (who will share the same nesting box) and two to enable you to segregate the young by sex. Some authorities suggest that when the young are weaned the mother should be put into another cage leaving the young in the cage they were born in.

Pregnancy

Pregnancy in the mouse lasts approximately 21 days with the rat's being a day or so longer. There are conflicting opinions as to whether the male rat should be left with the pregnant doe. However, the buck mouse should always be removed.

A few days before the litter is due the doe's cage should be cleaned and disinfected. Extra hay and other bedding material should be placed in the cage to provide her with adequate nesting material. Most births will occur at night and it is essential that the female should not be disturbed whilst giving birth otherwise she may eat the young. Mice give birth to between eight and 12 cubs with a record litter of 32. Rats produce between six and 16, the average litter for both mice and rats being ten. During birth the doe takes each cub as it is born, tear open the membranes and bites off the umbilical chord. The cubs are then licked clean and each afterbirth is eaten.

The young are born blind, deaf and hairless. The eyes do not open for about seven to eight days in mice and up to 14 days in rats. At about 10–14 days of age the incisor teeth will become visible and the young should be weaned at between two to four weeks of age. The sexes should be segregated to prevent breeding by six to seven weeks.

To prevent re-breeding of the female, the male should not be reintroduced as the doe can conceive from immediately after giving birth. Under these circumstances, if breeding was allowed to continue unchecked a female would produce more than 100 young in a year.

Milk

Insufficient milk production in the doe will lead to poor development in the litter. The mammary region should be checked for swelling to eliminate mastitis as a cause. If the problem is connected with insufficient milk, known as milk 'let down', close inspection of the nipples will reveal small wounds caused by excessive sucking in the cubs' vain attempts to obtain milk. One way to overcome this problem is to foster the litter on to another lactating female. The cubs must be carefully rolled on some floor covering moistened with the foster mother's urine. This is to disguise their scent to prevent the female killing them. The cubs are introduced into their new nest whilst the foster mother is temporarily removed. Trio breeding of mice with females sharing the same nest box facilitates fostering.

The average mouse litter is between eight and 12.

Rats are usually bred in pairs but fostering is very rarely required because the female can usually produce more than enough milk for her litter.

Mice should be retired from breeding after eight litters and rats after six litters.

Health

Provided that mice and rats have been correctly fed and the cage cleaned out regularly, they are usually extremely healthy animals. Cleanliness is very important to health in both mice and rats and the twice weekly cleaning scheme is set out below:

1) Remove animals to a second cage or secure carrying box.
2) Remove the cage substrate and bedding and dispose of it hygienically.
3) Wash out the cage with hot water containing a mild but safe disinfectant. Rinse in clean hot water and dry.
4) Wash, disinfect, rinse and dry all cage accessories. Return to the dry cage.
5) Add new substrate and new bedding to which a small amount of the old bedding has been mixed. This ensures the animal returns to a familiar smell.

Diseases

The importance of personal hygiene in the handling of rodents cannot be overstressed, and the 'rules of hygiene' are listed below:

1) Wash your hands after handling the mouse or rat, or after cleaning out the cage.
2) Wash the food dishes and water bottle separately from the household crockery.
3) Store all food separately from your own food in sealed containers to prevent access by vermin.
4) Animals must not be brought into contact with or be allowed on to work surfaces where food is prepared or into food storage areas or kitchens.

5) Never eat or drink whilst playing with a mouse or rat or when cleaning out the cage.

6) Young children must be supervised to ensure that these rules are kept.

Ailments If your mouse or rat is ill, seek veterinary advice as soon as possible. Unfortunately, with many of the diseases of mice, by the time the symptoms have been recognized, it is often too late for successful treatment. Whilst waiting for treatment, protect the animal's cage from draughts and keep it at an ambient temperature of approximately 20°C (68°F). The addition of soluble vitamins, available from most pet shops, to the water may prove useful.

There are a number of general signs of disease which you can identify in a sick mouse or rat. Diseased individuals are normally dull, although some may be extra lively or even turn aggressive. They may be relatively immobile and fail to move when stimulated. A hunched back, shrunken flanks and a ruffled dull coat along with discharges from eyes, ears or nose, are all signs to look for. Diarrhoea is an obvious clinical sign but it is not specific to any particular disease. Animals in a shocked condition or an advanced state of disease tend to have cold tails and feet when held in the hand.

Skin wounds and abscesses These are caused by fighting which is particularly common between males. The wounds become contaminated when in contact with the cage substrate and bedding and become infected. The infection can rapidly lead to the formation of an abscess. Veterinary attention must be sought as soon as possible to prevent further complications.

Ringworm is a fungal disease affecting the hair. Signs to look for are irregular areas of hair loss over the whole body, especially the head, flanks and tail. Veterinary attention should be sought without delay as this condition can be transmitted to humans. Affected animals should be put to sleep; treatment should not be attempted.

Overgrown teeth Overgrown incisor teeth can cause difficulties in eating, leading to a reduced appetite and weight loss. The teeth can be clipped to the correct length with nail clippers but unless remedial action is taken the condition will recur. To prevent this condition provide plenty of material for the mice and rats to gnaw.

Diarrhoea is very common in mice and rats and is associated with a wide range of conditions. Veterinary advice should be sought as soon as possible.

Respiratory disease This is one of the commonest problems of mice and rats. The affected animal will initially show loss of appetite, nasal discharge and abnormal breathing. If veterinary attention is not sought the condition will progress and the animal may adopt a hunched-up position with a ruffled coat. During treatment ensure that the ambient temperature, both during the day and night, remains between 18 and 20°C (64.5–68°F).

Paralysis can be caused by physical injury but if progressive it is more likely to be a viral disease. Any individuals showing general signs of ill health together with progressive paralysis should be put to sleep.

Middle ear infections This condition is more usually seen in rats. The clinical signs are obvious, the head being tilted towards the affected side. This results in circling and loss of balance. Antibiotic treatment from your veterinary surgeon may produce a complete recovery. However, many animals are left with a discernible tilt of the head.

Lymphocytic choriomeningitis A serious disease of mice that can be transmitted to humans. A mouse suffering from it will be very obviously ill, and must be taken to the vet. Mice bought from a reliable source should be free from this disease.

All rodents have a pair of incisor teeth at the front, separated from the cheek teeth by a small gap. These incisors grow constantly – the mouse or rat will gnaw hard objects to keep them short – but if they grow too long take your pet to the vet for treatment.

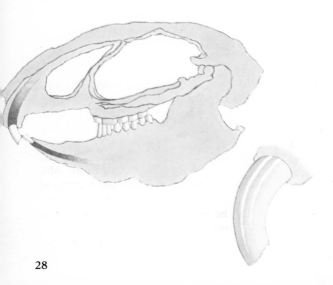

Exhibiting

Rats and mice bought from pet shops are unlikely to be of a high enough standard to exhibit at a show organized by the National Fancy Rat Society or National Mouse Club, but there may be classes at a local pet show for your 'pet' rat or mouse.

The National Mouse Club (NMC) was started in 1896 but the National Fancy Rat Society (NFRS) has only been formed since 1976. There are a number of local clubs affiliated to the NFRS and the NMC. These are the bodies which draw up the rules and standards by which mice are judged. These national organizations also hold shows for standard breeds and pedigree mice and rats. Details of these shows and exhibitions will be found in specialist magazines and newsletters. The local library should have the current addresses of the NMC and NFRS.

Animals to be exhibited must be in an extremely good condition to enter. There is usually a small entry fee. You will need at least three cages if you are to take up showing: a carrying box, which can be a modified plastic ice cream container; a grooming box; and the show cage. The grooming box is simple in design, merely being an escape-proof box with a thick layer of hay and clean sawdust in which the animal will burrow. Burrowing cleans and dries the fur but the glossy sheen on the coat requires that the fur be stroked with a silk cloth. Mice must be exhibited in the standard Maxey cage, coloured green outside and red inside, with only one mouse per cage. The cages can be bought from pet shops or from advertisements in magazines.

Rats are usually exhibited in plastic aquaria which are

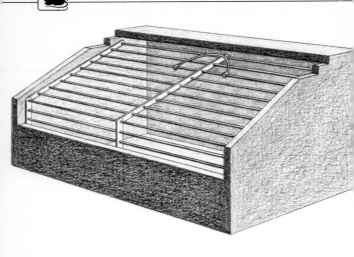

Above: the Maxey mouse show cage.

Right: aquariums with close-fitting wire mesh lids are used to show rats.

the standard show cages of the NFRS.

There are a number of points a judge will be looking for when assessing a mouse. The standard of excellence adopted by the National Mouse Club states that:
'The mouse must be long in the body, with long, clean head, not too fine or pointed at the nose; the eyes should be large, bold and prominent; the ears large and tulip-shaped, free from creases, carried erect with plenty of width between them. The body should be long and slim, a trifle arched over the loin, and racy in appearance; the tail, which must be thick at the root or set-on, gradually

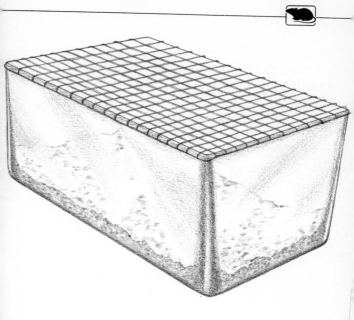

tapering like a whip lash to a fine end, the length being about equal to that of the mouse's body. The coat should be short, perfectly smooth, glossy and sleek to the hand. The mouse should be perfectly tractable and free from any vice and not subject to fits or other similar ailments. A mouse absent of whiskers, blind in one or both eyes, carrying external parasites, having a tumour, sore or patches of fur missing, suffering from any obvious disease or deformity or kinked tails shall be disqualified.' A judge can appoint marks up to a total of 100 points for a rat or mouse.

Index

DOCTOR WHO
SNAKEDANCE

DOCTOR WHO
SNAKEDANCE

Based on the BBC television serial by Christopher Bailey
by arrangement with the British Broadcasting Corporation

TERRANCE DICKS

Number 83 in the
Doctor Who Library

A TARGET BOOK

published by
the Paperback Division of
W. H. ALLEN & Co. PLC

A Target Book
Published in 1984
By the Paperback Division of
W. H. Allen & Co. PLC
44 Hill Street, London W1X 8LB

First published in Great Britain by
W. H. Allen & Co. Ltd, 1984

Printed and bound in Great Britain by
Anchor Brendon Ltd, Tiptree, Essex

ISBN 0 426 194578

The BBC producer of *Snakedance*
was John Nathan-Turner, the director
was Fiona Cumming.

Contents

1

Nightmare

On a rocky hillside between two great jagged stones sat
Dojjen the Snakedancer.

A gaunt, white-haired old man, he wore simple
leather garments as sun-bleached and serviceable as his
own wrinkled brown skin. He sat cross-legged, quite
motionless, staring wide-eyed into infinity. Thrust into
the ground at his side was his forked Snakedancer's
stick. A live snake was coiled around its head, emerald
eyes glinting, forked tongue flickering in and out.
Around Dojjen's neck hung a gem-stone pendant, the
blue crystal of the Snakedancers.

The crystal *glowed*.

'We are *not* where we are supposed to be!'

Nyssa came into the control room in time to hear the
Doctor's words. She felt no great surprise. In Nyssa's
experience, the TARDIS was very seldom where it was
supposed to be.

Nyssa looked expectantly at the Doctor. Now in his
fifth incarnation he was a slight, fair-haired youngish
man with a pleasant, open face. He was dressed in the
fawn frock-coat and striped trousers of an Edwardian
cricketer, and there was a fresh sprig of celery in his
buttonhole.

At the moment, it wasn't the Doctor's appearance
but Nyssa's own which concerned her. She was

awaiting the Doctor's reaction to her new outfit, a blue-and-white striped top with a white collar, and rainbow-striped skirt.

'Well?' she asked.

The Doctor gave her a distracted glance. The effect of the new outfit was both colourful and striking but it didn't make the slightest impression on him. 'We're not where we're supposed to be,' he repeated.

Nyssa gave him a 'what's-the-use' look. 'Where are we, then?'

'I don't know.' The Doctor studied the instruments. 'It's not a navigational malfunction.'

'Shall I wake Tegan?'

Tegan was their other companion, now sound asleep in her room.

'No need, there isn't any danger. It's puzzling, though. Very puzzling.'

Nyssa came to join him at the console and punched up navigational data on a read-out screen. 'Let's see where we are'. She read out the data. 'Planet G 139901 Kb in the Scrampus System. Local name: Manussa. Type 314S. Inhabited. Atmosphere, 98% Terran normal. Gravity, 96% Terran normal.'

'Well at least we can breathe the air, that's something.' He looked accusingly at her. 'You look different.'

'Yes, Doctor.'

'The question is, how did we get here?'

'There's more data. Third planet in Federation System. Status Colony. Former Homeworld Manussan Empire: Destroyed. Former Homeworld Sumaran Empire: Destroyed. Present Economy: Subsistence Agriculture and Tourism!'

'Former Homeworld?' interrupted the Doctor.

8

'Manussan Empire.'

'No, the other one.'

'Former Homeworld: Sumaran Empire.'

Strange that one insignificant planet should be the homeworld for two mighty empires, thought Nyssa. And stranger still that both empires should be swallowed up in barbarism.

The Doctor was checking instruments. 'This is serious, Nyssa. Someone's been playing about. Who set these co-ordinates?'

'You did.'

'No, no, no! You remember, I was trying to teach you and Tegan to read the star charts. One of you actually read out the co-ordinates for me to set. Who was it?'

Nyssa remembered quite clearly. She could *see* Tegan reading out the long string of co-ordinate numbers. But the Doctor was clearly put out by the error. Somehow it seemed unsporting to get her sleeping friend into trouble. 'I can't really remember, Doctor.'

'I can. It was Tegan!'

Tegan slept. She stirred a little. Her face twisted and she muttered incoherently. Tegan was dreaming.

In her dream, she stood before a cave. The area around the cave had been carved to resemble the head of a snake. The mouth of the snake formed the cave entrance. It loomed very large, and Tegan felt small, alone and afraid. Slowly and reluctantly she began walking towards the cave mouth, drawn by some irresistible power. She passed inside, looked up, and gave a gasp of horror. There, looming over her, was the skull of a giant snake. Somehow the skull was hideously alive, eyes glowing red, bony jaws opening and closing

9

angrily. The snake skull grew immense, filling the entire cave.

Tegan screamed.

Wrapping the scarlet lounging-robe about his body, the Lord Lon strolled out of his bedchamber and stood gazing disdainfully around him. He was occupying the finest guest suite in the Palace of Manussa. The room was luxuriously, even opulently furnished in a bewildering variety of styles. There were fur rugs, wall-hangings, tapestries, reclining couches, low tables and chairs and an astonishing variety of art objects from all periods of the planet's long and colourful history.

Manussa had been the ruling planet of two great star-empires, and it was now a colony planet of the all-powerful Federation of Three Worlds. The planet and its people were a melting-pot, a jumble of innumerable cultural influences. Most of them, thought Lon, were reflected in this very room.

Lon yawned and stretched, still querulous and disorientated by the journey from Federation Home-world. He was a tall, handsome young man, with the sleek, well-fed look of one born to wealth and privilege – not surprisingly, since Lon was the favoured son of the Federator of the Three Worlds. He strolled indolently across the room, and sank down onto a couch. On a table close by stood a statuette. He reached out and picked it up.

Beautifully carved from crystalline rock by some ancient, long-dead craftsman, the statuette was in the form of a coiled snake with a jewel in its mouth. Lon examined it with languid interest. It was primitive of course, but the workmanship was good . . .

Lon lay back on the couch, turning the statuette over

in his hands. There was something strangely fascinating about it.

Tegan's scream sent the Doctor and Nyssa running to her room. They found her sitting upright in bed, wide-eyed with terror.

'Tegan, what's the matter? What happened?' asked Nyssa.

'The dream. It was the dream . . .'

'The dream?' said the Doctor sharply. '*What* dream?'

'I can't remember. I can never remember.'

'But you've had this particular dream before?'

His tone was sharp, almost accusing, and Tegan's eyes filled with tears.

'Stop it, Doctor,' said Nyssa. 'You're upsetting her.'

The Doctor ignored her. 'You have, Tegan, haven't you?'

'Yes . . .'

'Always exactly the same dream?'

'Yes, I think so. The images fade so quickly.'

'But the feelings, the feelings of fear remain?'

Tegan nodded.

'Leave her alone, Doctor.' said Nyssa. 'It doesn't matter Tegan, you're awake now. It was only a dream.'

Tegan shook her head. 'No, it wasn't somehow. It was more than just a dream.' For a moment she looked almost haunted.

Nyssa was alarmed. 'Tegan, that's nonsense.'

'She means it,' said the Doctor quietly. 'And I think she could be right.'

Still toying with the statuette, Lon looked up as a handsome middle-aged woman in sumptuous rose-coloured robes came into the guest suite. Her jewelled

11

head-dress looked very like a crown. Indeed she was a queen in all but name. This was the Lady Tanha, Lon's mother, wife of the Federator.

Tanha had the gentle, practised charm of an experienced consort. A charm polished by countless state visits to provincial cities, innumerable official receptions and civic ceremonies, and endless demonstrations of folk dancing and native art. She was an intelligent, quietly determined woman, somewhat trapped in her never-ending role as the great lady. Tanha was frequently bored to extinction by her official duties, but over the years she had learned not to show it – unlike Lon. She looked at her son's lounging-robe in mild dismay. 'Lon, you're not dressed yet! Ambril will be here in a moment. He promised to show us the caves this morning, had you forgotten?'

Lon yawned. 'No, mother, I hadn't forgotten.'

'Well, then, we must make an effort.'

'Must we?'

'Well of course we must.'

'Why?'

'Because it's expected of us. You *are* the Federator's son.'

Lon gave her a long-suffering look.

She said gently. 'Come along, tell me what's wrong.'

Lon yawned again. 'What is wrong, mother, is that the Federator's son is bored . . .'

The Doctor was studying the TARDIS console when Tegan came into the control room. She was dressed in her white camisole top, and a light fawn jacket and skirt, and seemed fully recovered from her nightmare. Nyssa followed close behind.

'Now then, Tegan,' said the Doctor seriously. 'Where

12

are we?'

'What?'

'It's a very simple question. Where are we?'

'Aren't we on Earth?'

'No, we're not. So – where are we?'

'How should I know?'

'*Think*, Tegan. Think!'

Once again, the urgency of the Doctor's questioning seemed to leave Tegan puzzled and distressed. She stared miserably back at him, her eyes filling with tears.

'Doctor!' protested Nyssa.

In a more gentle voice the Doctor said. 'Please, Tegan, *think*! Reach back into the recesses of your mind.'

'Manussa . . . are we on Manussa?'

'Good! Well done, Tegan.'

'Well – are we?'

'Yes we are.'

Tegan gave him a puzzled stare. 'But – how did I know that?'

'Manussa,' said the Doctor thoughtfully. 'Formerly Homeworld of the Sumaran Empire – which may or may not ring a bell. Does it, Tegan? The Su-Maran Empire . . . The Empire of the Mara.'

Tanha was trying to persuade her son to take his official duties a little more seriously. 'You must learn to be tolerant, Lon. Oh, I agree, Director Ambril *is* rather trying, but he means well.' She smiled reminiscently. 'On the whole I rather preferred his predecessor. Now, what was the man's name? He was completely dotty, you know, but much more fun!'

'It's not just Ambril, Mother. It's all of it. The Ceremony of the Mara, *everything*. It's all such nonsense.'

'Is it?'

'Of course it is. The Mara was destroyed, what – five hundred years ago, and we're *still* celebrating the event. Why?'

'Why not? After all, the ceremony only happens every ten years.'

'It occurs to me,' said Lon cynically, 'that the whole thing is only kept going to remind the people here how much better life is under the Federation.'

'And so it is.' said Tanha placidly.

'Is it?'

'Of course it *is*. Life under the Mara must have been gruesome in the extreme.' Tanha indicated the statuette in Lon's hands. 'Just look at that thing. It's *grotesque*. You know Lon, you ought to take more interest in our heritage.'

'Really? Why?'

'It's the root of this world's culture, the Legend of the Return.· Though mind you, oh, what was the man's name, the director before Ambril . . . Anyway, he didn't think it was just a legend. He thought the Mara really would return.'

'Mother, am I supposed to take an interest in the ramblings of some madman?'

'Oh, he didn't *ramble*. He was very impressive in his way.'

'The Mara was destroyed,' said Lon emphatically. 'Not just banished to another dimension, but destroyed. It will not return "in a dream" or in any other form.'

'If you say so.'

'I think I just have!'

Tanha was not to be deterred. 'Well, it made a very

14

good story, anyway. Quite made my hair stand on end!'
She smiled reminiscently. 'Yes, Ambril's predecessor
was rather good value – even if he was talking nonsense . . .'

Still Dojjen sat motionless between the two great
stones, staring wide-eyed across the hills. The blue
pendant glowed on his lean brown chest, and beside
him the snake coiled lazily about the head of the
Snakedancer's staff.

Somehow it seemed that Dojjen's unblinking gaze
wasn't really turned on the surrounding hills at all. He
seemed to be looking inward. Waiting.

The Doctor rushed into the control room and said,
'There!' He was holding a small electronic device, a
little black box, with switches in the top. From the box
came two wires, terminating in ear-pieces. The whole
thing was slung on a thong, so that it could be worn
around the neck. It reminded Tegan of the portable
stereo sets that were just coming into use when she was
last on Earth. She stared at it.

'What's it for?'

'Hypnosis,' said the Doctor. He slipped the device
over Tegan's head, adjusting it until it was comfortable.

Nyssa looked on dubiously. 'Is this really necessary,
Doctor?'

'Yes! We must recover Tegan's dream, and hypnosis
is the quickest way.'

Worriedly, Nyssa studied Tegan's unhappy face.
'Why must we recover the dream?'

The Doctor was adjusting the controls on the device.
'Because dreams are very important! Never under-
estimate them. Once there was a man who fell

asleep and dreamt that he was a frog – who was dreaming of being a man. When he awoke he didn't know if he was a man who'd dreamt that he was a frog, or a frog dreaming he was a man.'

Tegan said flatly, 'I'm still possessed, aren't I Doctor? The Mara is still inside my head.'

The Doctor was silent for a moment, remembering events not so very long ago, on a planet called Deva Loka, the world of the Kinda. Tegan had indeed been possessed – by the Mara, an evil entity from some other dimension that manifested itself as a snake. Fortunately the Mara had passed on from Tegan's mind, choosing another victim, but Tegan had always feared that some trace of the Mara was still left inside her mind.

'Well?' demanded Tegan.

'We'll just have to see,' said the Doctor evasively.

'But that is what you think – isn't it?'

'It does seem likely. I'm sorry, Tegan.'

'But how, Doctor . . . *where?*'

'It's obviously below the level of conscious thought. Your waking mind is strong enough to resist it. But in sleep it loosens its grip, and the battle is joined.'

'The battle for what?'

'Control,' said the Doctor simply. 'There, that should do it.'

'So that's why Tegan mis-read the co-ordinates and brought us here,' said Nyssa slowly.

The Doctor nodded. 'There's a possibility that the Mara seized temporary control and brought itself home . . . Now then, Tegan. Insert the ear-pieces, try to relax and when switched on, listen to the sound.'

Tegan obeyed. A low soothing rushing sound filled her ears, punctuated by occasional bleeps.

The Doctor watched her intently, his face concerned.

16

Slowly she seemed to be relaxing. The battle for Tegan's mind was about to begin.

2

Cave of the Snake

Lon listened with weary indulgence as his mother rambled on about that earlier state visit to Manussa. She was particularly taken with her memories of the previous Director.

'He thought that the only people who knew the real truth about the Mara were the Snakedancers. Do you know, once he even took us to visit them? It was miles from anywhere, way up in the hills. Of course it was all madly unofficial. We had to go in disguise. Can you imagine, your father in disguise! I mean, even then . . .'

Lon smiled, recalling the stern dignity of the Federator. It was hard to imagine his father, even as a young man, taking part in so undignified an adventure. 'And did they?'

'Did who what?'

'Did these Snakedancers know the real truth about the Mara?'

'It was so dark and they were all so dirty it was difficult to tell,' said Tanha frankly. 'Oh they were frightful! They were all covered in ash, and some of them were almost naked. They lived on roots and berries and things, and they put themselves into trances. It was all *quite* disgusting. They handled live snakes, I remember . . .'

'Whatever for?'

'It was something to do with their religion.'

'And what did father think?'

'The Federator, as usual, was not amused . . .'

Lon chuckled.

There was a deferential tap upon the door. Tanha called, 'Come in.'

Director Ambril entered, splendid in his official black robes trimmed with purple, and his black fur hat.

He bowed low. 'Good morning, my Lady Tanha.'

'Good morning, Director Ambril.'

Ambril was a thin-faced, fussy man in his fifties. Far more of a scholar than a diplomat, he had accepted the post of Director of Historical Research solely because of the archaeological opportunities it presented. The art of the Sumaran era was a passion with Ambril. Showing two such distinguished visitors the historic sites of Manussa was a rare opportunity, and he meant to make the most of it.

He rubbed his hands eagerly. 'Are we all ready?'

Tanha sighed. 'Not quite, I'm afraid.'

She nodded towards the still supine Lon.

Ambril's face fell. 'Well, in that case, perhaps I should withdraw . . .'

'No, no, no. Please stay, Director. My son can dress *quite* quickly.' She looked imploringly at Lon, who didn't move.

Lon held up the little statue. 'What's this?'

Ambril peered at it. 'That, my Lord? It is a gift to you both. A small token in honour of your presence here, deputising for your father. I trust you approve.'

'Thank you,' said Tanha graciously.

Lon studied the statuette, making no reply.

Ambril looked at the statuette in Lon's careless hands. It had been quite a wrench to part with it. 'It is exquisite, is it not?'

'Is it a fake?' asked Lon insolently.

Ambril was shocked. 'Oh no, my Lord. It is from my own collection. It is seven hundred years old, from the middle Sumaran era. As a matter of fact, I unearthed it myself.'

'Did you really?'

'Yes, my Lord!'

'Here then, catch!' said Lon suddenly, and pretended to toss the statuette.

Ambril reached out with a gasp of horror – then relaxed, as he realised he was being teased. 'Oh, my Lord . . .'

Lon smiled, and – tossed the statue.

Ambril leaped forwards and caught it just in time.

Lon sauntered unhurriedly towards his bedchamber.

Tanha smiled apologetically at Ambril, who set the statuette down on a table with trembling hands. She really must talk to Lon about these little pranks, she thought. The boy could be so thoughtless at times.

Tegan lay stretched out on her bed, the device around her neck in operation.

'Tegan, where are you now?' asked the Doctor gently.

'On Deva Loka. The world of the Kinda . . .'

'What are you doing there?'

Tegan's voice came in anguished gasps. 'It's horrible. Something inside my head . . . If you must know, I climbed a tree and dropped apples on his head!' Her voice changed, becoming angry, fearful. 'No! I will never agree to what you ask, never . . .' The voice changed again. 'Doctor, am I free of the Mara now? Forever? *Am I?*'

'You must go deeper, Tegan,' said the Doctor. 'Go

deeper. Much deeper.'

Tegan's face relaxed. Suddenly she smiled.

'Where are you now, Tegan?'

'In my garden, silly.' The voice was that of a child. 'Everything grows in my garden, and people always come back. It always works. I can tell lies, too, and people don't always notice. I'm safe here.'

'How old are you?'

'I'm six, silly.'

'Tegan, you must leave your garden now.'

'Oh, why?' whined Tegan.

'To go still deeper,' commanded the Doctor. 'Deeper and further. Can you hear me, Tegan. I want you to go into the dream.'

Tegan stiffened in terror. 'No . . . *no!*'

'Why not?'

'*Because I mustn't!*'

The Doctor leaned over her. 'Tegan, you are perfectly safe. You must go into the dream.' He paused for a moment, studying Tegan's twitching face. 'Now, where are you?'

The words seemed almost forced from Tegan's lips. 'Cave. Snake mouth cave. Out . . . Out . . .'

'Out where?'

'I'm . . . *outside*. I'm being fed this image.'

'*Go in.*'

'No. Mustn't.'

The Doctor said remorselessly. 'Tegan, you must go into the cave. We need to know what's there.'

Tegan's eyes were screwed tightly shut. 'Something . . . in here. Over there. Mustn't look. Mustn't ever look. I'm safe if I don't look.'

'Tegan!'

'No . . . no . . .' gasped Tegan.

22

The Doctor's voice was firm. 'Tegan, you are perfectly safe. You must look. We need to know what is in there.'

Tegan's eyes opened wide. Slowly her head turned to her left and her face twisted with fear as she focused on some unseen horror. Suddenly the fear faded from her face, and it became cold and hard. She glared angrily at the Doctor and the voice that came from her lips was deep and harsh and terrible.

'*Go away!*'

The Doctor knew that the voice was not Tegan's voice. It was the voice of the Mara.

The old market quarter sprawled through the warren of streets that surrounded the palace. They were narrow, winding streets, roughly cobbled, and they were lined with shops and stalls and booths of every kind. Many of the stalls sold food and drink and the warm air was heavy with the smells of cooking fires, roast meats, baking pastries and spicy sweetmeats.

Manussans from all over the planet thronged the narrow alleys: lean brown hillmen, robed and hooded; richly dressed merchants and officials; brawny labourers; off-duty soldiers in steel and leather. They jostled through the ever-busy streets, eating and drinking, turning over the goods, buying and selling and haggling, laughing and chattering and arguing and crying their wares. Loudest of all were the showmen, bellowing the delights of the various attractions inside their booths.

One of the noisiest was Dugdale, a sturdy barrel-chested man with a voice like a bull. Resplendent in a military-looking tunic with tarnished gold froggings, a gold sash and a somewhat moth-eaten fur hat, Dugdale stood before his Hall of Mystery. On the front of the long booth there was painted a huge coiled snake, drawn in such a way that the entrance to the hall led through the mouth of the snake.

'Roll up,' roared Dugdale. 'How about you, sir? You Madam? Step this way if you would be so kind. I invite you to take the most exciting journey of all, the voyage inside. The journey to meet yourself.' The crowd ignored him. Undeterred, Dugdale ploughed on. 'I address you in the silence of your own hearts. I offer my personal challenge. Dare you bear witness to what the Mara shows? Dare you gaze upon the Unspeakable? Dare you come face to face with the finally Unfaceable?' He paused and added hopefully, 'Children half price!'

The crowd flowed unheedingly.

Dugdale sighed. Trade had been slack for weeks now, and for no good reason. Maybe it was the excitement of the approaching ceremony. Though you'd think that would increase the appeal of an attraction that dared to use the Mara itself as a come-on. He thought about going over to the tavern for a mug of wine to cool his throat.

Suddenly Dugdale spotted a swirl of movement just ahead. A tightly-knit little group was forcing its way along the street, burly guards clearing the way before them. Nobs, thought Dugdale in satisfaction. A party of aristocrats from the palace, out for a little slumming. The kind of people who carried purses full of gold coins. Hopefully, he raised his voice. 'Step this way, please. Come face to face with the truth about yourselves. Come along now, please.' The little group came level with his booth, and showed every sign of moving straight past it.

In desperation Dugdale stepped out in front of them,

addressing a richly-clad young man who strode a little ahead of the rest. 'You sir, for instance. You!'

The young man stopped, and looked coldly down at him. 'Are you addressing me?'

Undeterred, Dugdale pressed on with his spiel. 'Now, sir, you have the look of a humble seeker after life's truth.'

'Do I really?' There was a silky menace in the young man's voice.

'Of course you do! Now sir, if you'd care to step in-side . . .'

'Do you know who I am?'

A little crowd was gathering. Instinctively Dugdale played up to it. 'No, young man, I do not! Nor do these good people. Do tell us. Who are you?'

By now the crowd should have been joining in the mockery. But no one was laughing. The rest of the group had come up by now. Dugdale saw the richly dressed woman, and the high official hovering deferentially at her elbow, the brawny Federation bodyguards in their terrifying mask-like helmets.

Suddenly Dugdale's head felt loose upon his shoulders. He bowed low. 'I beg your pardon, my Lords, my Lady. 'I'm sure I didn't mean to give offence.'

To Dugdale's relief the woman smiled graciously, dismissing the incident. She moved on her way, escorted by the official and by her bodyguards. But the young man stayed where he was, sneering down at Dugdale. 'Well, what's in there?'

'In there?' babbled Dugdale.

'Yes. What exactly does one face in your shoddy little booth?'

'Mirrors, my Lord,' said Dugdale miserably.

'Mirrors?'

'Yes, my Lord. Distorting mirrors. That's all. People are amused.'

'Are they really?'

'Yes, my Lord. Generally.'

The woman had paused a little way ahead. 'Lon,' she called, 'Are you coming?'

'Coming, Mother.'

With a last chilling glance at Dugdale, the young man stalked away.

'*Lon*' thought Dugdale. He had been exercising his wit at the expense of the son of the Federator!

Dugdale leaned back against the façade of the Hall of Mirrors sweating with relief. He'd missed his purse of gold, but at least his head was still where it belonged.

The Doctor was making some adjustments to his hypnotic device. Tegan lay back on the bed, apparently quite calm and relaxed.

Nyssa said worriedly, 'That voice, Doctor, what was it?'

'The Mara – speaking through Tegan's mouth.'

Nyssa tried to remember the Doctor's account of events on Deva Loka. 'I thought you said there was a physical change when people were possessed by the Mara?'

'There is. It happens as the victim's mental resistance weakens. But this time I can prevent it.'

'How?'

The Doctor tapped the device round Tegan's neck. 'With this. It can be adjusted to inhibit the production of the brain waves associated with dreaming. It can't be used indefinitely, but it will give us a little time.'

'To do what?'

'We must find the cave – the cave of the snake mouth from Tegan's dream.'

'It's a real place then?'

'Oh yes,' said the Doctor definitely. 'What's more, I would guess that it's somewhere very close to us.'

The entrance of the Cave of the Snake was set into a low rocky hill on the outskirts of the oldest part of the city. The rock round the cave mouth had been carved into an elaborate snake's head, and, just as in Tegan's dream, the entrance of the cave formed the mouth of the snake. A flight of time-eroded stone steps led up to the gaping black hole.

'This,' said Ambril, 'is the entrance to the cave system itself.'

Tanha nodded, remembering. 'I had forgotten how impressive it is.'

Ambril looked pleased.

Lon, as usual, looked profoundly bored.

Emerging from the TARDIS, the Doctor, Nyssa and Tegan found themselves beside some empty booths in a quiet corner of the market-place. Tegan gazed calmly about her, looking rather as if she were sleepwalking.

The Doctor closed the TARDIS door behind them. 'Now, remember Nyssa, Tegan is experiencing total exclusion of all outside sound. You must be her ears.'

Nyssa nodded. 'But surely she can't dream now? She's awake.'

'Dreams are occurring in the mind all the time,' said the Doctor solemnly. 'Come on, we must hurry!'

By now, Ambril and his party had climbed the steps and were standing just inside the entrance to the cave.

They were in semi-darkness, though lights gleamed deeper in the caves.

Lon yelled into the darkness. 'Hello!' His voice echoed around the cave. 'Hello-o-o.'

Ambril winced. 'The cave system itself is a natural geological formation, worn out of the solid rock over hundreds of thousands of years by a now-vanished underground river.'

'Hello!' yelled Lon again. Again there came the echo. 'Hello-o-o.'

'Lon!' said Tanha reprovingly. She smiled apologetically at Ambril.

Ambril sighed and continued. 'The Chamber of the Mara is the largest natural cavern thus formed. Many of the most important archaeological finds –'

Lon was staring round the vast shadowy cave, 'Big isn't it?' he interrupted.

'Beg pardon, my Lord?'

'This place. It's big.'

'Yes, I suppose it is,' said Ambril patiently.

'Hello!' yelled Lon once again.

'Hello-o-o . . .' came the echoes.

Ambril sighed.

The Doctor, Nyssa and Tegan threaded their way through the bustling market. Nyssa and the Doctor looked round eagerly, taking in the noisy colourful scene. To Tegan in her silent world things were very different. She felt trapped in a meaningless confusion, filled with eerily-mouthing faces that made no sound. She could see the Doctor talking animatedly to a man at a nearby stall, and she saw the man pointing down one of the narrow side streets. The Doctor came back towards them.

'What did he say, Doctor?' asked Nyssa.

'I was right, it seems. There's a cave system at the edge of town, and the entrance fits the description exactly. It's this way.'

The Doctor led them towards the caves, uncertain what they would find there. One thing was certain. Only by finding and confronting the Mara once again, could he free Tegan's mind from the evil within.

3

Voice of the Mara

Still in his role of guide, Ambril ushered his party down the steeply sloping tunnel that led into the caves.

The entire cave system had been converted into a kind of rambling underground museum, with particularly interesting areas discreetly illuminated.

Ambril paused before one such section, a huge area of cave wall divided into separate panels, each panel covered with faded figures and symbols. Little stick-man figures were scattered about the panels, and it was noticeable that dotted energy lines from their heads came together in a diagrammed crystal which filled most of the last-but-one panel. The last panel of all was blank, as if the remains of the picture had been deliberately scraped away.

Ambril looked lovingly at the mural. 'This wall, known as the Pictogram, constitutes an invaluable record of the Sumaran era. Of course, academic interpretations of the precise meaning differ considerably. However, paying scrupulous attention to detail, and not allowing our imagination to run away with us, we can form the glimmering of an idea as to what these pictograms may mean . . .'

Ambril droned on and Tanha listened with her unvarying politeness.

Lon said abruptly. 'What about the Legend?'

Interrupted in mid lecture, Ambril blinked at him.

'The Legend, my Lord?'

'The Legend of the Return. Do you have an opinion?'

'Yes, my Lord, I'm rather afraid I do.'

'Well?'

Ambril drew himself up. 'The Legend of the Return is nonsense. Pure, superstitious nonsense invented by the people, simply to give themselves something with which to frighten their children. It has no basis, neither speculative nor proved, in historical fact!'

From the bottom of the long flight of steps, the Doctor stared up at the Cave of the Snake in admiration.

'Extraordinary, isn't it?'

Tegan was backing away, her face filled with terror.

Nyssa tugged at the Doctor's sleeve. 'Look, Doctor. Look at Tegan.'

The Doctor looked. 'This must be the cave from her dream.' He leaned forward. 'It's all right, Tegan, there's nothing to be frightened of.' He took her arm and tried to lead her up the steps.

Tegan pulled away. '*No!*'

'It's all right, Tegan,' said the Doctor again. 'There's nothing to be afraid of.'

Tegan backed away.

Nyssa said, 'Doctor, she can't hear you – remember?'

'Nevertheless, my dear Ambril,' Lon was saying, 'Your predecessor apparently believed in the Legend.'

'Yes, so he did!' said Tanha. 'Now what was the man's name?'

'His name was Dojjen, my lady,' said Ambril stiffly.

'Dojjen! Of course, that was it!' Tanha was delighted. 'Dojjen!'

'I am afraid Dojjen came to believe in so many

32

things,' said Ambril sadly. 'He became very erratic towards the end. Here in the cave system the real work was sadly neglected.'

'The real work?' asked Lon idly. 'Oh, I see. You mean poking about in the ruins. Digging for trinkets?'

'I mean *archaeology*, my Lord,' protested Ambril. 'I have tried to re-establish our work here on a scientific basis.'

'And I'm sure we are all very grateful,' said Tanha soothingly.

Ambril beamed. 'Shall we proceed into the Chamber of the Mara?'

Tegan was sitting on the top step of the flight that led up to the cave mouth, her back to the entrance of the cave. She was hunched forwards, her arms about her knees. It had taken all the Doctor's urgings to get her this far, and she would go no further.

'What are we going to do?' asked Nyssa. 'She *can't* go in. She's too frightened.'

'Well, you'll just have to stay with her. I'll go into the cave alone.'

The Doctor went up to the cave mouth, turned and gave them a reassuring wave and then went inside.

The most famous exhibit in the caves was the carving known as the Great Snake. It occupied almost the whole of one wall of the Chamber of the Mara. Immense, malevolent, terrifying, the huge serpent seemed about to spring out of the solid rock into which it was carved. Between the open jaws was an empty socket.

Ambril peered up at it. 'Exquisite is it not?'

Lon nodded towards the empty socket. 'What was in

33

its mouth?'

'The Great Crystal, my Lord. Purely decorative.'

'Where is it now? Is it lost?'

'Oh no, my Lord. It was removed from its socket when the Mara was destroyed. Traditionally, the safe keeping of the Great Crystal is the responsibility of the Director of Historical Research.'

'You, in other words?'

'At present I have that honour, my Lord,' And if anxious to change the subject, Ambril went on with his lecture. 'As you see, the image of the Mara is sculpted out of solid rock . . .'

Moving along the tunnel, the Doctor heard what sounded like the voice of some kind of tour guide. 'This imagery of the rearing snake is consistent throughout the mid-Sumaran period, with only insignificant variations . . .'

'Someone's very well-informed,' thought the Doctor. He headed towards the voice.

In the Chamber of the Mara, Ambril was still droning on. 'In the Sumaran Three period the head has a tendency to be marginally less pronounced, but in general . . .'

By now even Tanha was losing patience. 'Oh, do be quiet, Director,' she pleaded. 'Just for a moment!'

Ambril fell silent.

For a long moment they all stared up at the great carved snake. So realistic were the stone coils that they seemed to writhe and twist, as if trying to break free.

The Doctor came quietly into the chamber and stood watching the little group.

Tanha shuddered. 'It really is horrible. I'm so glad

the Legend of the Return is just a story.' She turned appealingly to Ambril. 'It is just a story, isn't it? You're quite sure?'

The Doctor stepped into view. 'No, I'm afraid it's not!'

Lady Tanha jumped, and gave a little scream. A huge helmeted figure stepped out of the shadows by the door and clamped a massive forearm across the Doctor's throat.

The Federation bodyguards were never far away.

Tegan still sat hunched up at the top of the steps outside the cave, watched anxiously by Nyssa.

A passing hawker decided that they were a couple of likely prospects and came ambling over with his tray.

Not surprisingly he was selling snakes, garishly-painted articulated toys that wriggled convincingly with the aid of a stick. 'Look here, ladies,' he called. 'Souvenir snakes, very nice, very good!'

Nyssa looked at the tray and waved him away. 'No thank you, not now.'

The hawker turned his attention to Tegan. Picking up a snake from the tray, he leaned over and wriggled the snake in her face. 'Souvenir snake, lady?'

Tegan couldn't hear his words of course, only the silent rushing sound of the Doctor's device. She looked up and saw the grimacing snake, the mouthing face of the hawker and behind him the snake-mouth entrance of the cave. Suddenly Tegan leaped to her feet. She thrust the hawker aside and ran down the steps, disappearing down the narrow street that led to the market quarter.

'Tegan, come back!' called Nyssa. Then, realising that shouting was useless, she ran down the steps after

Tegan.

The hawker shrugged his shoulders and wandered off.

The Doctor wriggled frantically, trying to keep his feet on the ground. 'There's really no need for this,' he gasped.

'This is a private view,' said Ambril indignantly. 'You have no business to be here.' He waved the bodyguard. 'Throw him out!'

The bodyguard looked to Lady Tanha for confirmation. She nodded, and he began heaving the struggling Doctor away. Lon, however, welcomed *any* interruption to Ambril's lecture. 'Wait!' he ordered. 'At least let the man have his say.'

'But why, my Lord,' spluttered Ambril. 'After all, the man is quite clearly deranged.'

'Is he?'

'Of course he is!'

'Lon, please,' said Tanha wearily. 'I really think the Director should deal with this.'

Still in the grip of the giant bodyguard, the Doctor shouted, 'Director? Director of what?'

Ambril drew himself up. 'I am Director of Research effort into the Sumaran era.'

'Are you indeed? Then you may be able to help.'

'I think not,' said Ambril haughtily. 'Throw the fellow out.'

'Just a moment, Ambril,' snapped Lon. 'First let him speak.' He smiled mockingly at his mother. 'After all, it has been suggested that I take more interest in our legends!'

The bodyguard released the Doctor who straightened his collar indignantly. 'I should think so too! Now then, I have something very important to tell you – about the Mara.'

Nyssa reached the far end of the street just in time to see Tegan disappearing into the market quarter. She tried to follow her, but Tegan was out of sight, lost in the teeming crowd. Giving up the hopeless search, Nyssa turned and headed back towards the Cave of the Snake.

Tegan meanwhile was still lost in her strange, silent world. Jostled by the crowds she stumbled along, staring wildly at the silently mouthing faces all around her. Suddenly it all became too much for her. The colourful crowded scene began spinning around like a kaleidoscope, and Tegan fainted, collapsing in a heap before a fortune-teller's booth – right at the feet of Madame Zara, the fortune-teller.

The Doctor's story of renewed danger from the Mara was meeting a sceptical response. Tanha looked baffled and Ambril was openly scornful.

Lon was the most sceptical of all. 'And where, according to you, is the Mara now?'

The Doctor said carefully, 'At present it exists as a latent force in the mind of my companion.'

'Does it really?'

'The Mara is using her dream to increase its power. Eventually it will take over her mind altogether – if it can. But I've put together a device to inhibit this, at least temporarily.'

'How very resourceful! And where is this young lady?' The mockery in Lon's tone was obvious now.

'She's outside. Why don't you come and meet her?'

Lon shrugged. 'Why not? Take us to her.'

'Certainly. If you'll follow me?'

The Doctor led them back along the access tunnel and outside the cave – where he saw Nyssa hurrying up the steps to meet him.

'Nyssa! Where's Tegan.'

'Is this your companion?' asked Lon.

The Doctor ignored him. 'What's happened, Nyssa?'

Nyssa was gasping for breath. 'She's gone, Doctor.'

Lon turned to Ambril and Tanha and said mockingly, 'Oh dear! She's gone, apparently. How sad!'

Nyssa told the Doctor what had happened. 'It all happened so quickly. She just took fright and ran.'

'You have disappointed me, Doctor,' said Lon. 'I really should have you punished.'

The Doctor said urgently, 'Come on, Nyssa, we must find her.'

The bodyguard took a step forward, his hand on his sword.

'Oh let them go,' said Lon wearily. 'After all, what's the point?'

The Doctor and Nyssa had no more luck in finding Tegan than Nyssa had on her own. The press of the crowd made it difficult to move at any speed, and it was impossible to pick out one person amongst so many.

'Oh, this is hopeless,' said the Doctor at last. 'She was frightened you say?'

'Terrified.'

'Well, let's go back to the TARDIS. She might try to find her way back there.'

But there was no sign of Tegan in the TARDIS either.

Nyssa looked despairingly at the Doctor. 'Where can she be?'

38

'Who knows? As long as she's wearing the anti-dreaming device she should still be safe.'

'And if she takes it off?'

'I don't know,' said the Doctor helplessly. 'I just don't know.' He began pacing about the control room. 'There's so much we don't know. Why has the Mara returned? Why now, after so long? What does it want?'

Tegan awoke to find herself slumped in a chair inside a cramped and gloomy booth. Faded red and green hangings draped the walls, and a sinister hooded figure was hovering over her. Tegan gasped and shrank back and the sinister figure pushed back its hood to reveal a plump, rather motherly face looking at her in concern.

Madame Zara patted Tegan's shoulder. 'There! Feeling better dear?'

Tegan stared blankly at her.

Madame Zara reached forward and slipped the ear-pieces from Tegan's ears. 'There, that's better. Can you hear me now?'

'No,' protested Tegan feebly. 'I mustn't take it off.'

'Why ever not?' said Madame Zara. She lifted the device from around Tegan's neck. 'What is it? What does it do?'

'I can't remember,' said Tegan haltingly. 'I mustn't . . .' She looked appealingly up at Madame Zara. 'Where am I?'

'In my little booth, dear. You passed out and they brought you in here. Are you feeling better?'

Tegan rubbed her hands over her eyes, trying desperately to regain her grip on reality. 'Yes . . . I don't know . . . am I?' She looked at the device. For some reason it was very important. '*Why* mustn't I . . . Please, who are you?'

'Madame Zara, dear, the fortune-teller. I see into the future. I expect it was the heat, and all the people . . .'

'I expect it was all the people,' repeated Tegan slowly.

'Of course, it was,' said Madame Zara chattily. 'It's easy to get confused in crowds, isn't it? Anyway, I'm glad you're feeling better.'

There was a small round black-draped table in the booth, with a gleaming crystal ball in the centre. Tegan's eyes seemed drawn to it. 'In that? You see the future in that?'

'Oh yes!' Madame Zara giggled. 'Well, between you and me, not really dear. I pretend. I flutter my fingers, gaze deep into the ball and then . . .' She shrugged.

Tegan stared at her. 'And then?'

'Then I make something up, whatever comes into my head. Whatever I think they want to hear, really – after all, they're paying! It doesn't do any harm, does it? Mind you it's astonishing what does come into your head – sometimes I amaze myself!'

Tegan was swaying to and fro in her chair. 'Is it . . . surprising . . . what is it . . .'

Madame Zara was alarmed. 'What is it dear? What's wrong?'

Suddenly Tegan sat bolt upright, and spoke in a deep harsh voice. 'Is it? *Is it surprising?*' There was a terrible, mocking laugh. '*Look now!*'

Madame Zara stared as if hypnotised into her own crystal ball. She saw swirling mists, then a gradually solidifying shape. The shape of a snake's skull, with gnashing, drooling jaws. She screamed in terror as the crystal ball shattered into a thousand pieces.

4

Hall of Mirrors

Madame Zara jumped up, still screaming in fear.

Tegan threw back her head and laughed, a harsh and terrifying laugh.

Then, cupping her chin in her hands, she stared fixedly at Madame Zara, seeming to drink in the woman's screams of terror with fierce satisfaction.

Tegan laughed again, and Madame Zara backed away, covering her face. When she looked again, Tegan was gone.

The Doctor and Nyssa were in conference in the TARDIS. 'The trouble is,' the Doctor was saying, 'We don't know nearly enough. Without more information, we're simply blundering around in the dark.'

'What about the TARDIS's data banks?'

The Doctor shook his head. 'This is the Mara's homeworld, remember. The answers we want are out there. I'll try the Director of Research again. Maybe I can make him listen this time.'

'What about me?'

'You have another go at looking for Tegan in the market-place. We'll meet back here.'

Quite a crowd had gathered outside Madame Zara's fortune-telling booth. It seemed that something very dramatic had happened inside. A couple of market officials were with the hysterical fortune-teller now.

Tegan stood in the middle of the crowd, watching with the others, malicious amusement on her face . . .

Pushing her way through the market-place, Nyssa was attracted by the bustle outside the booth. Instinctively she made her way towards it. She didn't see Tegan, but Tegan saw her. Nyssa felt a tap on her shoulder. She turned and saw Tegan, smiling strangely at her. 'Come to see the fun?'

'What fun?'

'The fortune-teller's having hysterics. She's still in there. She screamed and screamed and screamed!'

Nyssa looked curiously at her. It was unlike Tegan to take pleasure in someone's else's misfortune. 'Are you all right, Tegan? Where have you been?'

Tegan looked away, refusing to meet Nyssa's eye. 'Of course I'm all right. Why shouldn't I be?'

'You're not wearing the Doctor's anti-dreaming device.'

'I took it off,' said Tegan loftily. 'It wasn't necessary.'

'Tegan! What about the Mara?'

'Stop fussing! What Mara?' Tegan was jumping up and down to get a better view. 'Look, there she is, they're bringing her out!'

Nyssa looked and saw two men supporting a sobbing middle-aged woman, leading her out of the booth.

Tegan sniggered. 'She mustn't see me!'

To Nyssa's astonishment Tegan sank cross-legged to the ground covering her face like a child.

Nyssa watched as the fortune-teller was led away, then looked down at Tegan. Tegan looked cunningly up at her. 'You should have seen her face though! It was so *funny*! She screamed and screamed and screamed. You could see right down her throat!' Tegan looked away again.

Nyssa leaned down, took Tegan's chin in her hand, and forced Tegan to look her in the face. 'What's the matter with you? What's been going on? Tegan, look at me!'

Tegan stared up at her, defiantly at first, and then the façade of confident defiance crumbled, leaving an air of utter misery. 'Nyssa, help me,' she whispered. '*I made it appear!*'

'Made what appear?'

Tegan's face and voice changed dramatically. '*You fool! Leave me alone!*' She sprang to her feet. '*Just leave me alone!*' Thrusting Nyssa aside, Tegan disappeared into the crows.

'Tegan, come back!' called Nyssa.'

She hurried after her.'

The offices of the Director of Historical Research would have been luxurious if they hadn't been so cluttered with artefacts from every period of Sumaran history. Some were sorted and classified, some still waiting Ambril's attention. Ambril's work was his life and he spent most of his waking hours in this room. At the far end of the room was a dining area and a table, upon which a servant was laying dinner.

Ambril was studying an ancient scroll at his desk when a curly-haired young man entered, wearing the brown robes and white collar of a sub-official. This was Chela, Ambril's assistant. He was a solemn young man who took his duties very seriously. He stood waiting deferentially by Ambril's desk.

Ambril looked up. 'Yes, Chela, what is it?'

'He's here,' said Chela excitedly. 'The man you were telling me about. The man from the cave!'

43

'Oh, *that* man! No, I can't possibly spare the time to see him. Tell him to go away.'

Never one for hanging about in ante-rooms, the Doctor strode in. 'Hello!' he said cheerfully.

Ambril sighed. 'Well, since you're here . . . Mind you, I know exactly what you want!'

'You do?'

'You've come to pester me with some more of the extravagant theories you've dreamed up concerning the Mara.' Ambril rose. 'Moreover, should I, the Director, fail to take sufficient notice of your colourful theories, it will mean the end of Civilisation As We Know It. How am I doing so far?'

'If you'd only *listen*,' began the Doctor.

Ambril interrupted him. 'I'm sorry to disappoint you, but you know, you're hardly the first. For some reason the study of the Sumaran Era has always attracted more than its fair share of cranks. And they seem particularly numerous whenever a ceremony is due.'

'What ceremony?'

'The Ceremony of the Mara. Every ten years, we celebrate the end of the Mara's rule and its final destruction by the Federation. Surprise me. Tell me you didn't know!'

'Exactly when is this ceremony to be held?'

'Tomorrow.'

'Impossible,' said the Doctor firmly. 'It must be called off, at least till my companion is found.'

'Oh certainly,' said Ambril airily.

The Doctor was taken aback. 'What?'

'A whole year of preparation, the Federator's son as guest of honour, but don't you worry, I'll just cancel the whole thing!' This time the mockery in Ambril's voice

44

was plain. 'Now if you'll excuse me? My assistant here will show you out.'

Chela came forward, but the Doctor waved him away. 'Look, won't you at least consider the facts? First of all my companion brought us here, to this world, without ever having heard of it before. Now, why should she do that? Why *here*? Secondly, I was able to use hypnosis to establish the presence of the Mara in her mind. She has this recurring dream, you see, and in the dream – '

Chela said, 'A dream? Did you say a dream?' He looked significantly at Ambril.

'It proves nothing,' said Ambril hurriedly. 'Merely that he is acquainted with the Legend.'

'Of course,' said the Doctor. 'The Legend of the Return.'

Chela nodded. 'According to the Legend . . .'

'Don't encourage him Chela,' snapped Ambril.

'Director, please,' said Chela. 'What harm can it do?'

Ambril threw his hands in the air. 'All right all right! Humour him if you must, Chela. But remember – where the Legend is concerned there are no actual facts to impede the full flow of the popular imagination!'

Chela turned to the Doctor. 'According to the Legend, the Mara was not destroyed by the founders of the Federation, but only banished.'

'To the Dark Places of the Inside?'

Chela nodded. 'According to the Legend, the Mara will return in a dream.'

'What does it want?'

'The Legend foretells that the Mara will return to regain its power over men when the minds meet again in the Great Crystal.'

Ambril had been listening with increasing unease.

45

'That's enough, Chela.'

'But how can minds meet?' demanded the Doctor. 'What does it mean?'

'What indeed,' said Ambril crossly. 'It's wishy-washy mystical mumbo-jumbo.'

'But Director,' protested Chela. 'What about the Snakedancers?'

'More mumbo-jumbo. It appeals to certain types of mind. Lazy, primitive, uneducated minds mostly. I'm sorry to see that even my assistant isn't immune. You'll find that the Legend becomes more and more vague the more you try to elicit any kind of factual detail.' Ambril rose and began pacing about the room. 'I'm afraid this kind of mystical vagueness pervades the entire culture.' Glancing about the room, he snatched something from a shelf and held it up. 'Now take this, for example.'

Ambril was holding a kind of ornate head-dress. It was surmounted by an elaborate crest which consisted of a number of face-masks in the shape of a fan. Ambril's voice took on his lecturer's drone. 'This particular artefact dates from the middle Sumaran era, and, unusually, is mentioned quite specifically in the Legend. There can be no doubt, the reference is to the 'Six Faces of Delusion'. Triumphantly Ambril held up the head-dress. 'Well, now, count the faces. One, two, three, four, five . . . You will observe that there are only five masks. Five faces, not six as the Legend would have it! Now, my point is this. I do find it extraordinarily difficult to take seriously a Legend that cannot even count accurately.' Ambril stroked the head-dress lovingly. 'Of course, artistically, it's an entirely different matter. The piece is exquisite, an undoubted masterpiece.'

The Doctor said thoughtfully. 'It's a head-dress you

say? A kind of hat?'

'Yes.'

'Try it on,' suggested the Doctor suddenly.

'What?'

'Try it on!'

'Certainly not! Whatever for?'

'Please, I just want to demonstrate something. Then I'll go and leave you in peace.'

'Oh, very well.' Awkwardly, Ambril perched the hat on top of his head.

The Doctor looked at Chela. 'Now, count the faces.'

Chela looked blank.

'Do as he says,' ordered Ambril.

Chela counted. There were the masks, of course. 'One, two, three, four, five . . .' Chela saw the puzzled face of Ambril beneath the head-dress. Catching the Doctor's eye he gave an involuntary smile.

'Exactly,' said the Doctor. 'And one more makes six. The sixth Face of Delusion is the wearer's own. That was probably the idea, don't you think?'

Ambril was spluttering with rage. 'Out. Get out! Go on, get out!'

The Doctor moved hurriedly towards the door.

Struggling to keep his face straight, Chela hurried after him.

Nyssa stood in one of the market streets looking anxiously about her. Although she hadn't managed to catch up with Tegan she'd managed to keep her in sight at least for a time. Now Tegan seemed to have vanished. Choosing a direction more or less at random, Nyssa went on with her search.

As soon as she was out of sight Tegan stepped out of her hiding place – which was in fact the entrance to

47

Dugdale's Hall of Mirrors. The Hall had been temporarily deserted by its weary proprietor, who was consoling himself with a mug of wine at the local tavern. Tegan was about to move away, when suddenly she changed her mind. She turned and went into the Hall.

Retracing her steps, Nyssa found herself outside the abandoned fortune-teller's booth. She remembered that somehow Tegan had been concerned in whatever had happened there. She went up to the doorway. 'Hello! Anyone there?' No answer. Nyssa slipped inside.

Peering round in the gloom she saw the fragments of the shattered crystal ball. And there, on the table, was the Doctor's anti-dreaming device. Nyssa picked it up.

Tegan passed through the tiny vestibule and through a curtained door into the Hall itself. It wasn't really much of a hall, just a long tent-room. It was lined with mirrors, ranged along the walls. Each mirror was framed with a crudely-drawn snake mouth, a kind of parody of the Cave of the Snake.

Tegan looked in the first mirror, and saw herself as a dumpy dwarf. She looked in the second, and saw an impossibly tall, elongated Tegan. She looked in the third mirror – and saw the Mara.

5

The Sign of the Mara

The giant snake-skull filled the entire mirror. Tegan backed away in horror, trying not to look. 'No no,' she whispered. 'Please.'

The Mara said '*Face me!*'

The voice was deep and harsh, the Mara voice, but it was coming from Tegan's lips.

Tegan shook her head. 'No, no . . . I mustn't. I can't.'

'*Face me!*'

'I'm so tired.'

'*Then borrow my strength.*'

Tegan struggled to regain control of her own mind. 'How is it possible? On the Kinda world the Mara was repelled by mirrors.'

'*On the Kinda world, I was trapped in a circle of mirrors,*' said the hateful voice. '*There is no circle here.*'

Tegan rubbed a hand over her eyes. 'Why am I so confused?'

'*You are divided against yourself. A stranger in your own mind. You are pathetic.*'

Tegan closed her eyes.

'*Look at me!*' commanded the Mara. '*I can make up your mind!*'

'No,' muttered Tegan weakly. 'No. . .'

'*Why not? What are you afraid of? Just who do you think you are?*'

In spite of herself, Tegan straightened up and stared

49

full into the mirror. The Mara snake-skull seemed to glow brighter for a moment, then slowly faded away.

Tegan looked down at her left arm and saw the mark of the Mara. A snake design ran down her forearm, the head of the snake on the back of her hand.

Tegan – or rather the Mara inside her – smiled, a cold, triumphant smile.

The Mara was in command.

The Doctor walked back through the market, pushing his way abstractedly through the crowds.

He heard a voice calling out behind him. 'Doctor! Doctor, wait.'

He turned and saw Chela running after him.

The Doctor waited and Chela hurried up to him, glancing over his shoulder to see that he wasn't observed. 'Here, Doctor, take this.'

Chela thrust something into the Doctor's hands. It was a pendant, a blue crystal on a golden chain.

The Doctor examined it. 'What is it?'

'The Snakedancers use them in their rituals. They call them "Little Mind's Eye". In the Legend, the Great Crystal is called the "Great Mind's Eye" '.

'Indeed?' said the Doctor thoughtfully.

'Perhaps there's a connection,' said Chela. 'Perhaps they're even made of the same substance. I just don't know. I wanted to run tests on this one, but Ambril wouldn't let me.'

The Doctor weighed the pendant in his hand. 'Why are you telling me all this?'

'I must go.'

'Wait,' said the Doctor. 'Tell me, Chela, do you believe in the Legend of the Return?'

'No, of course not.'

Chela turned and hurried away.

The Doctor called after him. 'One more question – who are the Snakedancers?'

But Chela had disappeared into the crowd.

The Doctor stood gazing after him, the crystal pendant in his hand.

He held it up to the light, looking into the blue depths of the stone.

Tegan stood looking into the mirror, unaware that she was being watched.

Dugdale had returned to his Hall of Mirrors some little time ago, and found, to his astonishment, a girl standing before one of his mirrors talking to herself in two completely different voices. Born showman that he was, Dugdale's first reaction, once he was over his astonishment, was to think that here was a talent that could be put to good commercial use.

He stepped forward, applauding ironically. 'Highly convincing, young lady. A trick of course, voice projection, the art of the ventriloquist, perhaps. Two voices in different registers. Very original, all in all!'

Tegan stood staring at her reflection, ignoring him completely.

Dugdale walked around her, studying her throughtfully. 'Now, various possibilities present themselves immediately. Should you be interested in something along the lines of . . . A partnership, perhaps? Me outside enticing the passers-by, talking 'em in, relieving them at the door of some small token of their sincere interest. You inside in the half-dark talking away to yourself in two voices – and scaring them half to death. Highly satisfactory all round. What do you think?'

Still no reply.

Dugdale was getting impatient. 'All right, my girl, enough's enough. I said I was impressed . . . as impressed as I need to be. I'm not a curious man – though I was once.' He gave a self-mocking laugh. 'I was once a long time ago, a Humble Student of Life's Mysteries, a Treader of the Secret Pathways, a Delver into the Darker Corners, and so forth. At the end of the day, when the lights come up – as they always do come up in one form or another – there's always someone standing with their hand out waiting to be paid. I decided long ago that person might as well be me. Or, in present circumstances – us!'

Suddenly Tegan swung round to face him. She spoke in the harsh, compelling Mara voice. '*Who exactly are you?*' She studied him. '*You are not important. There is only one who is important. Only he matters in what is to be done here.*'

Dugdale shrunk back, transfixed by her hypnotic glare.

Swinging the pendant throughtfully, the Doctor walked on. Once again he heard running footsteps behind him, and turned. This time he saw Nyssa.

'Doctor,' she gasped. 'I saw Tegan. I spoke to her.'

'Where is she?'

'I don't know. She ran away from me. I lost her in the crowd. Doctor, look!'

Nyssa held out the anti-dreaming device. 'She wasn't wearing this when I found her – and she was acting very oddly.'

She told the Doctor of Tegan's strange manner, and of finding the device in the fortune-teller's booth.

The Doctor listened keenly. 'When you saw Tegan – was she marked?'

'What?'

52

'On her arm – the mark of a snake.'

'I didn't see . . .'

'It's the Mara,' said the Doctor fiercely. 'It must be.'

Tucking the device in his pocket he strode away, Nyssa hurrying after him.

Lon had resumed his usual supine position, stretched out on the couch, gazing vaguely into space.

His mother appeared, sumptuously robed in blue and gold, and wearing a jewelled head-dress. 'Isn't it time you were changed, Lon? Lon? We're having dinner with Ambril, remember?'

'I'm not coming.'

'Good,' said Tanha briskly.

Lon didn't like having his sulks ignored. 'I beg your pardon?'

'Good,' repeated Tanha. 'It's probably just as well, you'd only spoil things anyway. Your behaviour in the caves this morning was unforgivable. Poor Ambril was quite disconcerted. You were taking advantage of your position.'

Lon yawned, and turned away. 'Oh please, if you're going to be dreary.'

'I am not going to be anything. We are invited to dinner, and I am going. Are you just going to lie there being bored?'

Lon stretched and smiled lazily at her. 'Yes, do you know I rather suspect I am. After all, what else is there to do?'

Tanha walked majestically to the doorway. She paused on the threshold. 'Oh, Lon, do come to dinner.'

Lon turned ostentatiously away.

Tanha sighed, and swept out of the room.

The Doctor marched Nyssa swiftly through the market and down the long narrow road that led to the Cave of the Snake.

Running up the steps he paused by the entrance, waiting for Nyssa to catch up. 'Come on!'

'What are we doing here?'

'I need facts, Nyssa, more facts. There's something I noticed here earlier. I need to take a closer look.'

They plunged through the snake-mouth and into the darkness of the tunnel.

As they walked along it Nyssa asked, 'Take a closer look at what?'

'The Pictogram. There's a ceremony taking place here tomorrow, commemorating the supposed destruction of the Mara.'

'So?'

'The Mara has waited a long time for its return. I think it plans to be – spectacular.'

When they reached the Pictogram the Doctor stood gazing at it absorbedly, taking in the little stick-men, and the dotted lines that ran from their heads to the crystal in the last panel.

'There, look, Nyssa, what do you make of that?'

Nyssa shrugged helplessly.

'Look,' said the Doctor. He pointed to the drawing of the crystal. 'That could represent the Great Crystal, couldn't it?'

'I suppose so.'

'And these lines represent energy of some sort?'

Nyssa nodded. 'Mental energy, perhaps. The lines go from the crystal to the heads of the figures.'

'Minds meet in the Great Crystal,' mused the Doctor. He pointed to the demon figures, lurking in the background of the Pictogram. 'Everything in this pictogram tells us something, if you know how to read it. So – what are these?'

Lon's half-doze was interrupted by a discreet tap on the door. He opened his eyes. 'Who is it?'

The door opened revealing a palace attendant. Behind him in the corridor loomed the inevitable figure of the bodyguard. The attendant bowed. 'There is someone here, my Lord. He insists that he must see you. Shall I send him away?'

Lon considered. Any break in the boredom was welcome. 'No, let him come in.'

The attendant disappeared and a moment later Dugdale entered the chamber looking around in awe, bowing and scraping with every step. 'Excuse me for intruding, my Lord.'

Lon stared at him, and then laughed. 'Oh, the showman!'

'I'm flattered you remember me, my Lord.'

'I remember your impertinence. Go away.'

'Our previous encounter was rather unfortunate, my Lord. Heat of the moment, press of the crowd, various misunderstandings . . . and so forth.'

'What do you want?' snarled Lon.

Dugdale swallowed hard and said miserably. 'I've been sent to fetch you.'

'Have you indeed!'

Dugdale stumbled on. 'Yes my Lord. You are summoned.'

Lon sat up and stared menacingly at the terrified showman. 'Summoned? *I* am summoned! How extraordinary. By whom?'

The Doctor was on all fours peering at a figure in the

bottom of the Pictogram. Nyssa had moved on into the Chamber of the Mara, where she was looking at the great carved snake.

'Doctor!' she called.

The Doctor got up, dusted his knees and came to join her. 'What?'

'If the Great Crystal of the Legend really existed – then, logically, that is where it would have fitted.' Nyssa pointed to the blank socket between the snake's jaws.

The Doctor stepped back, studying the terrifying snake carving. Things were beginning to come together. 'Yes, of course, it's obvious.'

'What is?'

He led the way back to the Pictogram. 'The Great Crystal . . . The Great Mind's Eye. The lines do represent a flow of mental energy, but not going to the figures, coming *from* them.'

'And meeting in the Great Crystal?'

The Doctor nodded. 'Just as a lens focuses the rays of the sun, the Great Mind's Eye gathered all the individual thought-energies and concentrated and amplified them.' The Doctor indicated the last, blank panel. 'Redirecting them, presumably, there!'

'But it's been scratched out!'

The Doctor turned and strode back into the main chamber. 'Now, according to the Legend, the Great Crystal is the source of the Mara's power. But where is it now? What exactly are its properties? If only I could get a look at the Great Crystal itself . . . unless . . .' The Doctor fished the crystal pendant from his pocket, and stared thoughtfully at it. 'Unless . . . Come on, Nyssa.'

'Where to?'

'Back to the TARDIS. We're going to try an experiment!'

Dugdale paused outside his Hall of Mirrors, waving Lon forward. 'In here, my Lord.'

Lon stared at him. 'Here – in your Hall of Mirrors? I hope for your sake I'm not going to be disappointed?' Lon had listened with amused disbelief to Dugdale's story of a strange girl with extraordinary powers who insisted on seeing him. Some local girl he supposed, drawn by the glamour of his great position, spinning a fantastic tale to arouse his interest. He had decided to go along with the game, just as long as he found it amusing.

Dugdale gave him an anguished look. 'Please, my Lord. She's waiting inside.'

'Can I have your personal assurance?'

'She's inside,' repeated Dugdale.

'So I should hope,' said Lon.

He went into the booth.

A little uncertainly Lon moved through the darkened hall. He smiled when he saw Tegan standing before the mirror. So, there *was* a girl after all. Quite an attractive one. He advanced towards her. 'You summoned me. It's not something I'm accustomed to, but here I am.'

For a moment Tegan took no notice of him.

'Well?' said Lon impatiently. 'What happens now?'

Tegan turned slowly towards him. He saw there was a reddening about her eyes and mouth. She held out her hand. Lon smiled. It was just as he had expected. 'Yes . . . after all, why not?'

He took Tegan's hand – and was immediately transfixed as a current of energy flowed between them. Frightened, he tried to pull away, but Tegan's grip held him powerless. In the mirror behind him, there appeared the snake-skull of the Mara.

Suddenly Lon relaxed. He looked wonderingly down

at his hand, the one Tegan was holding. On the back of his forearm, as on Tegan's, was the design of the snake.

The Mara had marked another follower.

6

Dinner with Ambril

Very delicately and unobtrusively, the Lady Tanha stifled a yawn.

Ambril's little dinner party had just begun. Various local dignitaries had paid their respects and withdrawn to a discreet distance. Now she was trapped with her host, who was launched into yet another interminable lecture on his favourite, and indeed only, topic of conversation.

Ambril droned on. 'And, then, you see, my Lady, we draw a complete blank. It's quite clear that the Manussan's of the *Pre*-Sumaran era were a highly civilised people. Their technology, in some respects, was considerably in advance of our own. And suddenly, almost overnight, the Manussan civilisation simply disappeared. Evidently it was subjected to a cultural catastrophe of unimaginable proportions.'

By now Tanha was hungry as well as bored. 'Shall we eat?' she suggested brightly.

Ambril was too absorbed to hear her. 'Yes indeed, to such an extent that when the Federation records begin, some six hundred years later, they speak of the Manussans as a primitive people, in thrall to the Mara, sunk in barbarity, degredation and cruelty.'

Lady Tanha stifled another yawn, a big one this time.

Ambril peered worriedly at her. 'Are you all right, my Lady?'

Lady Tanha smiled and nodded. 'Yes, yes of course, do go on.'

'What a shame your son was indisposed this evening.'

Lady Tanha sighed. 'Yes indeed. I'm sure he would have found it all *most* illuminating.'

Lon was striding up and down the Hall of Mirrors, staring at the distorted reflections, and laughing hysterically.

'Silence,' said Tegan.

The laughter stopped, as if cut off by a switch.

Tegan turned and walked stiffly out of the door.

Instantly Lon followed her.

By now, Dugdale was wondering what the devil he was getting himself into. Whatever it was, it was too late to draw back now. Miserably he trailed after them.

The Doctor sat cross-legged on the floor of the TARDIS control room holding the Snakedancer crystal between finger and thumb.

Nyssa sat cross-legged opposite him. 'Doctor, I'm not at all clear what we're supposed to be doing.'

'Just think about it!'

'About what? What *are* we doing?'

'A simple test. If the Great Crystal focuses thought in some way, if this is the same sort of crystal it should exhibit some of the same properties. So, we must direct our thoughts at it, and see what happens.'

'All right, Doctor, if you say so. Now?'

'Yes. Now!'

Nothing happened.

After several minutes Nyssa opened her eyes, and stood up. 'I'm sorry, Doctor, I just can't seem to concentrate hard enough. I feel so foolish.'

The Doctor was thinking hard. 'Never mind. We'll try another way.'

He fished the anti-dreaming device out of his pocket and began making careful adjustments.

Nyssa watched him puzzled. 'What are you doing?'

'I'm adjusting the frequency – as an aid to concentration. There!' The Doctor slipped the device over his head and slipped in the ear-pieces. 'Right, let's try again. Now then, you just stay there. Watch the crystal closely and observe any changes. Are you ready?'

Nyssa nodded.

'Right,' said the Doctor. He closed his eyes frowning in concentration.

Nyssa stared fixedly at the crystal. For a moment it seemed as if this experiment too would be a failure. But suddenly the little crystal began to glow, brighter and brighter . . .

Nyssa gasped. 'That's impossible!'

The Doctor opened his eyes and the glow faded.

'What happened?' he asked.

Nyssa told him.

The Doctor looked thoughtfully at the crystal. 'It's only small, of course, but the potential power . . .'

Nyssa couldn't see what the Doctor was so excited about. 'All it did was glow with a blue light.'

'You're missing the point. It's not *what* you saw, it's the fact that you saw anything at all. It proves that the crystal has the power of transforming thought into energy. Perhaps even into matter itself. Don't you see? Just think of the power the Great Crystal must have. Whatever is in your thoughts, in your mind, it can actually make it occur!'

'And if the Mara is in Tegan's mind . . .' said Nyssa slowly.

'Exactly! The Mara needs the Great Crystal in order to make itself reoccur . . .' The Doctor leaped up and headed for the door. 'You'd better stay here, Nyssa, in case Tegan returns. I'll be back as soon as I can.'

'Where are you going?'

'To warn Ambril. He knows where the Great Crystal is. I've *got* to make him listen.'

Tegan strode swiftly up the steps that led to the Cave of the Snake and on into the tunnel. Lon, who was close behind her, paused for a moment waiting for Dugdale who was puffing along behind. 'Come along, Showman. Hurry up'

'Where's she taking us?' gasped Dugdale.

'Come on,' repeated Lon.

Dugdale hung back. 'I don't like this . . .'

Lon reached out and gripped his arm.

Looking down, Dugdale saw the snake-design on Lon's arm.

'Come on,' said Lon yet again, and dragged Dugdale into the cave.

They found Tegan in the Chamber of the Mara, staring angrily up at the empty jaws of the great carved snake.

She swung round, speaking in the deep harsh voice of the Mara. *'Who has dared to remove the Great Crystal? Where is the Crystal?'*

Without waiting for a reply, she stepped forward and pressed the snake-mark on her arm against the wall. With a heavy grinding sound a section of wall at the base of the snake-carving rolled back, revealing a small inner chamber. Tegan moved inside and the others followed.

Dugdale paused in the doorway, looking round. They were in a small stone room, thick with dust. It seemed to be completely empty, except for some kind of rubbish heap in the corner. Dugdale looked more closely, and saw that the rubbish consisted of gold and silver plates, crystal goblets, intricately-carved statuettes, rings and bracelets and necklaces, wrist and head-bands . . . There were precious objects of every kind, all covered in a thick coating of dust and grime.

Dugdale ran forward and began scrabbling in the pile. He snatched up a crystal goblet and polished it with the edge of his coat. Lon stood watching, a faint smile on his face.

'You are not impressed?' asked Tegan.

'Not overly – did you expect me to be?'

Tegan looked down at Dugdale. '*Leave them alone.*'

'You don't understand what there is here . . .'

'Toys for children,' sneered Lon.

Dugdale was frantic with excitement. 'Toys? These are the real thing. The genuine article. They're worth money – a fortune.'

Tegan beckoned imperiously. Reluctantly Dugdale got to his feet and stood staring wistfully down at the pile of treasure.

Tegan turned to Lon. 'Now, tell me about the Great Crystal. That interests me. It interests me very much indeed. Do you know where it is?'

'Yes, as a matter of fact I do.'

'Where?' demanded Tegan fiercely.

'To be more precise,' said Lon. 'I know who knows where it is.' He plucked the crystal goblet from Dugdale's fingers. 'And I know how he may be persuaded to tell us!'

Ambril's dinner was coming to an end at last. Flanked by Ambril and his assistant Chela, Lady Tanha sat smiling graciously at the head of the table. She had a terrible feeling that Ambril was about to make a speech. He raised his glass. 'A toast! To the Federation, as embodied in the person of this gracious lady!'

But before he could utter another word the Doctor hotly pursued by a number of attendants, burst into the room and skidded to a halt before the table.

The bodyguard behind Lady Tanha's chair dropped his hand to the hilt of his sword.

'Where is the Great Mind's Eye?' shouted the Doctor

'The what?'

'The Great Crystal, the one that was taken from the head of the snake in the Chamber of the Mara.'

Ambril turned deferentially to Lady Tanha. 'I beg your pardon for this interruption, my Lady, I will have the man removed . . .'

The Doctor leaned over the table, staring accusingly at Ambril. 'You know where it is!'

'I certainly do.'

'Where?'

'Wherever it is, I assure you it is perfectly safe.'

'You don't understand,' said the Doctor frantically. 'The Great Crystal is the *source* of the Mara's power. It needs that power to make itself reoccur. That is how it plans to return.'

'I think we've heard enough,' said Ambril. 'Take him away.'

At a nod from Lady Tanha, the giant bodyguard advanced on the Doctor, great hands outstretched.

'You don't understand,' shouted the Doctor. 'Through the Great Crystal the Mara will reoccur, as a physical fact – here on Manussa!'

The bodyguard closed in.

Dugdale stood in the secret chamber, the treasure of a lifetime piled in a dusty heap at his feet. Tegan and Lon were finishing a rapid conference. Both turned and looked at Dugdale.

'So,' said Lon. 'Only one problem remains.'

Dugdale gulped. 'Me? Oh, I could assist in your enterprise in whatever capacity . . . using my discretion.'

Tegan and Lon clasped their snake-marked hands.

'Or alternatively,' babbled Dugdale, 'I could simply forget. Whichever and whatever you prefer.'

Tegan glanced at Lon. 'He has served his purpose.'

Lon smiled coldly at Dugdale. 'You are no longer necessary.'

'Look at me,' commanded Tegan.

Dugdale tried to hide his face in his hands.

'No,' he sobbed. 'No. What are you doing?'

'Look at me,' commanded Tegan's voice. 'I'm not going to harm you. *Look at me!*'

Unwillingly Dugdale looked up and realised to his horror that Tegan's voice was coming from Lon's mouth.

'*That's right,*' said the Mara cruelly. '*Look at me! Look at me!*'

Dugdale looked fearfully down at the linked snake-marked hands, and then up into Tegan's face. Her eyes glowed fiery red . . .

7

Dojjen's Journal

The Doctor was in a cell. It was a large cage-like affair in a grey metal prison area, and it looked uncomfortably escape-proof. Chela, Ambril's assistant, came into the cell carrying a small tray. 'I have brought you food and drink, Doctor.'

'How long am I going to be locked up?'

Chela offered the tray. 'Don't you want it?'

'Thank you,' said the Doctor, rather ungraciously. He reached through the bars and took bread, a variety of fruits, and a jug of water from the tray. 'Come on, how long are they keeping me here, at least you can tell me that.'

'You are to be kept here until after this afternoon's ceremony.'

'That will be too late! Whatever happens will happen *at* the ceremony.' The Doctor forced himself to calm down. 'Listen to me, Chela . . .'

Managing to eat and drink at the same time, the Doctor gave Chela an account of what he had so far learned, about the Mara and its plans to return.

Chela said wonderingly. 'It is hard to believe, Doctor.'

'Do you think I'm inventing it all? What would I have to gain?'

'I don't know. Perhaps Ambril is right, and you are deluded.'

'But you're not sure?' challenged the Doctor. 'You're not sure it's all nonsense – are you?'

'Of course I am.'

'Then why did you give me that crystal?'

Reluctantly Chela said, 'Because you are not the first to hold such views. Dojjen, the Director before Ambril . . . he too was convinced that the Mara would return.'

'What happened to him?'

Chela hesitated. 'It doesn't matter. The Great Crystal is safe in Ambril's charge.'

He left the prison area.

The Doctor slammed his fists against the bars in frustration.

The showman Dugdale stood in a corner of the secret chamber, rigid, motionless, a living corpse.

'You will leave him like that?' Lon asked.

'He may still be useful,' replied Tegan dismissively. 'He is not important. Only the Great Crystal is important. I must have it!'

Lon picked a crystal goblet from the pile of treasures and tucked it into his tunic. 'I will do all I can.'

'*You must not fail me.*' It was the Mara, speaking through Tegan's mouth.

Lon studied the snake pattern on his arm. 'No. I understand.'

He left the secret chamber and the door closed behind him.

The Lady Tanha was breakfasting when Lon came into the guest suite. He paused, taken aback at the sight of her. Instinctively he concealed his left arm behind him. Tanha pushed aside her dish of toasted grains and fruit. 'Lon! Where have you been?'

'Oh, out there.'

'Come here.'

'Whatever for?'

'I want to look at you,' said Tanha indulgently. 'I nearly raised the alarm when I realised your room was empty last night, but I didn't want to embarrass you.'

'Embarrass me?'

Tanha smiled fondly. 'If you were not amusing yourself last night . . . having fun while your poor mother was being bored to tiny pieces at that official dinner – well, I shall never forgive you.'

'No, Mother, as it happens I wasn't out having fun.'

'Really? You promise?' said Tanha teasingly. She noticed the hand behind his back. What are you hiding?'

Lon gave her an angry look. 'What?'

'There's something in your hand, isn't there? Show me!'

Relieved, Lon transferred the goblet from left hand to right, and held it out to his mother. She examined it with interest. 'It's antique, isn't it?'

'It's just a cheap fake. I picked it up in the market.'

'Since when have you been interested in such things?'

'It caught my eye, that's all,' said Lon impatiently. 'Mother! I will not have you continually asking questions!' He stormed off to his room, leaving the goblet in Lady Tanha's hands.

She stared after him in astonishment. She knew in her heart that Lon was spoiled, though she also liked to think there was no real harm in him. But the vicious anger in his manner was something new. For a moment he had seemed almost like a different person.

Nyssa spent an uneasy night in the TARDIS. When the

69

Doctor still hadn't returned next day she had decided to go to the palace and look for him.

Assuming that the Doctor was (a) in trouble and (b) probably locked up, Nyssa had persuaded a friendly kitchen servant to direct her to the prison area. Now she was moving cautiously through the palace corridors towards it. She ducked back out of sight as a tall, curly-haired young man came along the corridor and turned into the doorway of one of the larger rooms.

Chela found Ambril at his desk, immersed in the study of a tattered leather-covered notebook. He looked up impatiently. 'Well?'

'I've taken our prisoner some food.'

'I hope he's grateful.' Ambril returned to his book, realised his assistant was still there and looked up. 'Is there something else, Chela?'

Chela bit his lip, and then blurted out, 'I think he's harmless.'

'Harmless? Of course the poor fool's harmless. We'll let him go after the ceremony.'

'He *is* a doctor . . .'

'Doctor of what?' asked Ambril scornfully. 'I'm sure the man has no academic standing whatever!'

As Nyssa approached the prison area she heard a familiar voice. 'No, I do not want more blankets. All I want is to get out of here. Be good enough to tell your master I want to see him.' A door at the end of the corridor opened and an angry palace servant carrying a pile of blankets emerged. Slamming the door behind him, he turned and walked off in the opposite direction.

Pleased to find her theories confirmed, Nyssa headed towards the prison area. On the other side of the door she found a corridor, giving on to a row of cage-like cells with slanting metal bars. Only one of the cells was occupied. Pacing up and down inside it was the Doctor. 'Nyssa,' he said delightedly.

Nyssa ran towards him, clasping his hands through the bars.

Lon came out of his bedchamber. He had washed and changed his clothes and he was wearing elbow-high gauntlets that conveniently hid the snake design on his arm.

Lady Tanha was still holding the goblet, and Lon stretched out his hand. 'Give it to me!'

Lady Tanha handed it over. Lon turned and marched from the room.

'Where are you going?' called Lady Tanha.

But there was no reply. She looked worriedly after him.

Chela was still lingering in the Director's office, and by now Ambril had got used to his presence. He pushed aside the journal and looked up. 'Just look at this, Chela!'

'What is it, Director?'

'The meanderings of another crank – like your friend the Doctor.' He tossed Chela the book. 'It was written by Dojjen – in the months before he decided that his particular line of research was best pursued up in the hills with a snake wrapped round his neck!' Ambril snorted. 'You'll find the last entry of interest – mental health interest, that is! Dojjen addresses what remains of his wits to the question, "Where is the Mara?" '

Chela turned to the end of the journal.

Ambril waved his hand impatiently. 'Well, why

71

don't you read it out?'

Chela struggled to decipher the thin spidery hand-writing. 'Where the Winds of Restlessness blow. Where the Fires of Greed burn. Where Hatred chills the blood. Here! In the Great Mind's Eye. Here in the depths of the human heart. Here is the Mara.'

'You see,' said Ambril triumphantly.

'Is it a code, Director?'

'Code? Of course it's not a code. It's nonsense. Pure and simple, woolly-minded nonsense.'

'I'm very pleased to hear it,' said a voice from the doorway. It was Lon.

Ambril rose and bowed. 'My Lord.'

'Good morning to you both,' said Lon pleasantly. 'I need to ask a favour of you, Director.' He glanced at Chela. 'A private favour, if you don't mind?'

'Of course, of course, why should he mind,' said Ambril. 'Out, Chela, out, out, out!'

Chela bowed and withdrew.

Ambril turned eagerly to Lon. 'And now, my Lord how may I serve you?'

Nyssa soon realised that although she had found the Doctor she was powerless to free him.

The cell had a heavy old-fashioned lock, and it was firmly closed. Nyssa rattled the door angrily.

'It's no use, Nyssa, I've already tried that!'

'But this is so stupid!'

The Doctor said wryly, 'The lock's very primitive, you see. Practically a museum piece. No electronic impulse matrix to decode, no sonic micro circuitry to disrupt. Just a crude, mechanical six-barrel lock movement, operated by a very large key. Primitive but adequate – more than adequate actually, since the key is what we don't have.'

'There must be something we can do!'

They heard approaching footsteps.

'Quick, hide!' said the Doctor.

Nyssa looked frantically for a hiding-place, but before she found one Chela entered, carrying a leather-bound book. He nodded to Nyssa as if taking her presence for granted.

'Well?' demanded the Doctor. 'Have you come to let me out?'

'I have brought you this, Doctor. It was written by Dojjen. Look at the last page.'

'I'd sooner you unlocked the door and let me out,' grumbled the Doctor as he took the book.

'I can't do that.'

'Why not? Don't you have the key?'

'No, as it happens, I don't.'

'Ambril does, I suppose,' suggested the Doctor casually. 'I imagine he keeps the key in his rooms?'

'Yes, as a matter of fact he does,' said Chela impatiently. 'I thought you'd be interested in Dojjen's book, Doctor, but if you can't be bothered . . .'

'No, wait, wait,' said the Doctor. 'Of course I'm interested. The last page you say?'

The Doctor opened the book – and made a discreet 'off-you-go' signal to Nyssa over Chela's shoulder. As the Doctor began studying the book, Nyssa edged behind Chela's back and slipped quietly out of the cell area.

Lon had made his request.

Ambril was shocked and horrified. 'My Lord, I am bound by my oath of office. An oath, dating back to the time of the destruction of the Mara.'

'But you do know where the Great Crystal is?'

'Yes, my Lord. But not even the Federator himself may actually see the Great Crystal. However, may I say how grateful I am by your renewed interest in our antiquities.'

'Well, you know how it is,' said Lon casually. 'With time on one's hand one pokes around. Surprising what one can turn up – like this, for instance.' He held out a carved crystal goblet.

Ambril stared at it in astonishment for a moment, and then took it from him with trembling hands. Snatching up a magnifying glass from the desk he studied it eagerly. He looked up, eyes shining. 'My Lord, where did you find this? Where did you find it? I must know.'

Lon stared at him in mock astonishment, and Ambril said apologetically, 'Oh my Lord, I'm sorry to be so insistent, but you don't realise what a find like this means to me.'

'Is it valuable?'

'It is beyond price.'

'And rare?'

'It is unique, my Lord.'

'How strange! I found a sort of cache you see, a secret chamber. It was when I was poking about in the cave system. There seemed to be lots of things like that, as far as I could see. They were scattered around rather, I picked this one up at random.'

'Scattered?' gasped Ambril. 'But . . . how many? . . .'

'I really didn't count.'

'There were *many* such objects though, my Lord?' Ambril's voice was trembling. 'Many? Lots? My Lord, tell me!'

Lon smiled. 'Perhaps you'd like me to show you

where they are?' he suggested casually.

Ambril stared at him, open-mouthed.

The Doctor looked up from Dojjen's journal, rubbing his chin thoughtfully.

'Well?' asked Chela eagerly.

The Doctor tapped the book. 'I see he refers to "The Great Mind's Eye"... When was this journal written?'

'It was the last thing Dojjen did before –'

'Before what?'

'Nothing. Give me back the book.'

'Before he what?'

'Before he danced the Dance of the Snake.'

The Doctor stared at him in astonishment. 'Dojjen? But I thought the Snakedance was banned by the Federation?'

'It was, nearly a hundred years ago.'

'Why were they so against it?'

'According to the Legend, the Return of the Mara could only be resisted by those of a perfectly clear mind. The dance was a dance of purification, in readiness to combat the return.' Chela shrugged. 'However, the Federation held that since the Mara no longer existed the dance was no longer necessary. They banned the dance and drove the Snakedancers into the hills.'

'Why were they so against the dance?'

'Apparently it involved the use of – certain powers.'

'What kind of powers?'

'Mental powers – of a kind easily misunderstood – or misused.'

'Yes, of course...'

Nyssa found Ambril's rooms without difficulty, slipped inside and began to search for the key to the Doctor's cell. Since the place was so cluttered, her search was not an easy one. But she found the key at last, inside a carved wooden box. As her fingers closed upon it a voice behind her said, 'And what do you think you are doing?'

Nyssa whirled round.

There in the doorway stood a handsome middle-aged woman in sumptuous rose-coloured robes, a tiara gleaming in her hair.

Behind her in the corridor was a giant bodyguard.

8

The Origin of Evil

Nyssa tried to run, but the bodyguard was too quick for her. Grabbing her as she tried to dodge past, he seized her arms with hands like metal clamps and dragged her back into the room.

Lady Tanha regarded her prisoner uneasily. 'Where is Ambril, he really should be here. I am really not sure what to do . . . This is not a situation to which one is accustomed.' She took the key from Nyssa's hand and said politely. 'I think perhaps you'd better come with me. Isn't that what one usually says in these circumstances?'

Pleased to have found an acceptable formula, Lady Tanha nodded to the bodyguard and left the room. The bodyguard followed, bringing Nyssa with him.

There was a puppet-show in the market. Hordes of enthusiastic children, and some adults too, gathered round to watch the beaky-nosed figure of the villain-hero as he attacked and abused his wife, chased off the Federation civic guard, and was finally swallowed up by a giant puppet snake which rose from the depths of the little booth.

Ambril stood staring at it unseeingly. He was in a fever of impatience. Lon had led him here, then left him while he went off to another stall. But to Ambril's relief, he saw Lon returning, carrying a couple of lanterns.

They were paper lanterns, the kind carried during the ceremony, made of rice-paper with a candle inside, and painted in garish snake-patterns.

'Here we are,' said Lon. 'Just what we need.'

'What are they for, my Lord?'

'Oh, we must be properly equipped.'

'But where are we going?'

'Just you wait and see. Come on.'

Lon led the astonished Director through the crowd.

The Doctor was still absorbed in Dojjen's journal. 'So Dojjen believed the Legend of the Mara to such an extent he gave up everything and went up into the hills to purify himself in readiness?'

'He was mad,' said Chela uneasily. 'Nobody believes in the Legend these days.'

The door opened and Lady Tanha appeared.

'My Lady,' said Chela in astonishment.

'Bring her in,' ordered Tanha.

The bodyguard marched Nyssa into the cell area. Almost apologetically Tanha said, 'I'm afraid I have another prisoner for you.'

Lon and Ambril had reached the top of the flight of steps.

By now the entrance to the Cave of the Snake was draped with festive banners and bunting, in honour of the coming ceremony. Ambril looked at Lon in astonishment. 'In there? My Lord? But that's impossible. All the passages have been thoroughly explored over the years.'

'That's what you think,' said Lon cheerfully. 'Come along.' He paused. 'No, wait a moment, we might as well do this properly.' He slipped a scarf from around his neck. 'One moment, Director.'

'My Lord what is this?' spluttered Ambril, pulling away.

'A blindfold.'

'Certainly not!'

'You don't have to wear it,' said Lon negligently. 'It just depends how much you want the honour of making this important archaeological discovery on your own.'

'You would allow *me* the credit?'

'Certainly,' Lon held up the blindfold. 'It's up to you!'

'Very well.'

Nervously Ambril came forward, and let Lon tie the scarf about his eyes.

Chela ushered Lady Tanha back into Ambril's room, and watched her return the key to the desk. 'I caught the girl quite by chance,' she said. 'I was actually looking for my son.'

'He was here, my Lady. Apparently he had something confidential to discuss with the Director.'

'Did he really? How odd. How very odd!'

Lon complicated Ambril's blindfold journey as much as he could, leading him stumbling up and down the cave passages. But eventually he led the apprehensive Director to the entrance to the secret chamber, opening it, as had Tegan, with the pressure of the snake-mark on his arm against a section of the rock.

'Forward,' directed Lon. 'Another three steps. Now wait there. Now, over the step, three more steps forwards and stop.' As the door closed behind them, Lon slipped the blindfold from Ambril's eyes. 'There! You've done splendidly.'

Ambril peered around the chamber, which was illuminated only by the faint yellow light of the lanterns.

Lon pointed. 'Over there. I trust you will not be disappointed.'

Like Dugdale before him, Ambril saw the treasures piled carelessly in the corner and was overwhelmed. He knelt reverently to examine them. 'Disappointed, my Lord? No indeed!'

'It was all worth it, then?'

Ambril was examining the treasures with trembling hands. 'My Lord the very existence of these objects . . .' he said brokenly. 'So entirely unexpected. It's amazing, my Lord, this is the greatest moment . . .' Ambril moved his lantern to reveal more of the treasure trove. The little circle of light illuminated Dugdale's booted feet.

Slowly Ambril raised the lantern, revealing Dugdale's blank, staring face. For a moment the showman gave no reaction to the light. Then suddenly he jerked into life like an automaton. 'Roll up, roll up, wonderful entertainment, children half price. Step this way please for the Spectacle of a Lifetime. Tread the misty corridors of Time. Visit the dark and distant shores of the imagination . . .' The cracked voice cut out as suddenly as it had begun.

Ambril looked at Lon in horror. 'Where am I? What is this place?'

A harsh voice spoke from the shadows. '*Stop wasting time.*' Tegan stepped forward, red-eyed, red-mouthed, '*Where is the Great Crystal?*'

Ambril looked round wildly. He made a pathetic attempt at a laugh. 'It's all a hoax, isn't it, my Lord? Just a prank at my expense? There are some noble friends of yours, aren't they? It *is* all an elaborate hoax – isn't it?'

Lon jabbed at the pile of treasures with his foot, 'And these?' He took a fine porcelain vase from Ambril's hands. 'Are they part of the hoax? After all, you're the expert.'

He opened his hands, and the vase dropped from his hands, shattering on the stone floor.

'No,' screamed Ambril. 'No!'

Through Tegan's mouth the Mara spoke again. *'Where is the Great Crystal?'*

'Why?' said Ambril distractedly. 'Why is everyone so interested in the Great Crystal?'

'Everyone?' said Lon.

'Who else?' demanded Tegan.

Ambril looked at their threatening faces. 'Oh, some crank . . .'

Tegan moved closer. *'His name?'*

'He calls himself the Doctor, although personally I rather doubt that he has the right – '

'The Doctor must not interfere,' hissed Tegan. 'He must be killed.'

Ambril looked at her in horror. 'Killed?'

'Forget the Doctor,' said Lon. 'You see, Director, my friend Tegan here has a theory. In order to test it, the Great Crystal must be placed in its socket during the Ceremony.'

'No! That is quite impossible!'

'Nothing is impossible,' said Tegan flatly.

Lon bent down and scooped up a double handful of precious objects. 'Now listen to me, Ambril. If you do not co-operate, I will guarantee that you will never set eyes on any of these trinkets again. *I* shall destroy them. And you will always know that they existed – somewhere.' He dashed a figurine to the ground. 'That you discovered them – once.' A vase followed the figurine. 'Held them in your hands – once.' Another crystal goblet shattered. 'And then lost them – *forever*. It's up to you.'

Ambril could have resisted bribes or threats but to watch the wanton destruction of irreplaceable antiques was more than he could bear. 'No, wait,' he sobbed. 'All right, I agree. I'll do as you ask.'

The Doctor was still locked up in his cell. The difference was that now he had Nyssa for company.

To Nyssa's exasperation, the Doctor was sitting placidly on his bunk reading Dojjen's journal.

'What are we going to do, Doctor?'

The Doctor looked up. 'Shush!' He went on reading.

'*Doctor!*'

He looked up again. 'Well, what do you suggest?'

'We've got to get out of here.'

'How?'

'If only we still had the sonic screwdriver!'

'Well, we haven't,' said the Doctor mildly. 'So for the time being we must make good use of what we do have.'

'And what's that?'

'This!' said the Doctor tapping Dojjen's journal. He passed it to Nyssa. 'Here, try it.'

Nyssa took the diary and started to read it, reluctantly at first, then with increasing interest. The Doctor sat waiting patiently.

Time passed.

Eventually Nyssa looked up. 'It's fascinating, Doctor. But does it help us?'

The Doctor rose and began pacing about the cell. 'That journal is a record of a journey. A private, mental journey. Dojjen must have discovered something that finally decided him.'

'But to do with what?'

The Doctor shrugged. 'The Mara, the history of this planet, the origins of the crystals . . .'

Suddenly a theory was forming in Nyssa's mind. 'To function as they do, the crystals must possess a perfect molecular structure, attuned to the exact wavelengths of the human mind. Doctor, the crystals are man-made. They must be!'

The Doctor stared at her. 'Yes, of course, I should have realised.' He took the crystal pendant from his pocket and studied it. 'It has to be structurally perfect, free of all flaws and distortions, even the minute distortion induced by the effects of gravity.' The Doctor's mind was racing now as he built up his theory. 'The crystals, including the Great Crystal, must have been designed by a people who had mastered the techniques of molecular engineering in a zero-gravity environment.'

'But the Manussans aren't that advanced.'

'Not now – but according to Chela, this crystal is eight hundred years old.'

Nyssa said, 'If the Manussans had been a people capable of sophisticated molecular engineering eight hundred years ago – their civilisation wouldn't have just vanished. There would be records, at least, probably all kinds of traces.'

'Not necessarily,' said the Doctor. 'I suspect that when they made the Great Crystal they overlooked one vital factor. The nature of the mental energy absorbed would determine the nature of the matter created. Suppose the Great Crystal absorbed only the evil that was in their minds, the restlessness, the hatred, the greed, absorbed it, amplified it, reflected it – '

'And created the Mara!' whispered Nyssa.

'Exactly! And in the reign of evil which followed, they must have forgotten the most important thing of all – that the Mara was something that they themselves had blindly brought into being.'

9

Death Sentence

Ambril found himself blinking in the sunshine outside the Cave of the Snake. He looked wildly about him. Lon had insisted on blindfolding him again before taking him out of the hidden chamber, and now Ambril was haunted by the thought that his new-found treasures might be lost to him forever.

He turned to Lon. 'The objects you showed me, the antiques . . . Please, where are they?'

'They are quite safe,' said Lon soothingly. '*If* you co-operate fully, you will be able to 'discover' them again – after the ceremony.'

'And your friend – that strange girl –'

'She will look after them for you. Now, come, we must get back to your quarters. You have arrangements to make.' He put a hand on Ambril's arm, 'And remember, co-operate, and *you* can discover the treasures after the ceremony. The credit will be yours – all yours!'

Tegan stood motionless in the lantern-lit chamber, her eyes glowing fiercely red.

She held out her left hand, palm down in front of her, staring at the snake design, concentrating fiercely. To Dugdale's fascinated horror, the snake began to pulse and swell. Somehow it became a *real* snake.

'Well, Showman,' sneered Tegan. 'Do you still

85

dream of my success? Perhaps you do. It will be greater than you could imagine! You have no choice you know. You have to look.'

The snake grew larger.

Still Dojjen sat motionless between the two jagged rocks, the crystal at his throat growing brightly, the snake twisting lazily around the staff.

There was a fierce alertness to his concentration now. He sensed that the danger for which he had prepared for so many long years was very close . . .

'If Dojjen had worked out what happened – ' began Nyssa.

'Only some of it,' interrupted the Doctor. 'The rest he must have learned from his contact with the Snake-dancers. They'd kept the old knowledge alive, hidden in traditions and legends.'

'So Dojjen became convinced the Mara would return?'

'That's right. But he didn't know exactly when – and anyway, nobody would listen to him. Just as no one will listen to us!'

'But Dojjen was Director for a time. Why didn't he simply destroy the Great Crystal when it was in his charge?'

'Good question . . . and I don't know the answer.'

'So now we've worked it all out, what do we do now?'

'We wait,' said the Doctor simply.

Picking up Dojjen's journal, he sat down on the bunk and resumed his reading.

Lady Tanha was talking to Chela in Ambril's room. She found the young man's company very soothing.

Chela was quiet and respectful, and she felt sure that she could rely on his discretion.

'My poor Lon,' she was saying. 'It's difficult for him you see. He is young, impatient. He knows that one day he will be Federator and rule over the Three Worlds. My husband is an old man but he is – lingering on, rather. He could live for many years yet, and so my son must wait.' She looked thoughtfully at Chela. 'The young do not like to wait, do they, as a rule? You may speak freely, strictly between ourselves.'

Chela was petrified with fear and embarrassment. It was dangerous enough to listen to this kind of talk, let alone join in.

Lon and Ambril appeared in the doorway and Chela was shocked to see that the usually meticulous Director was grimy, dishevelled, and showing strong evidence of suppressed excitement. He might almost have been drunk.

'Lon!' said Tanha reproachfully. 'Where have you been?'

'Nowhere, Mother, just – exploring. Ambril here has been showing me round the Caves again, haven't you Ambril?'

Ambril didn't seem able to reply.

Nyssa was rapidly approaching explosion point, pacing up and down the cell like a captive animal. 'How *can* you just sit there, Doctor?'

'Patience, Nyssa, patience. I have an idea we may be out of here soon.'

'Oh yes?'

'Young Chela was far more convinced than he let on. I think he'll help us.'

'And if he doesn't?'

87

'I think he will.'

'But you can't be sure, can you?'

'No,' said the Doctor gently. 'I can't be sure.'

Nyssa resumed her pacing. 'And meanwhile Tegan is in the power of the Mara. Unless we can help her soon, it will destroy her.'

Lon was dusting Ambril down rather like a father whose child has been playing in the mud. 'All my fault, I'm afraid, I did rather insist. We explored the deepest recesses of the caves you see. I'm afraid he got himself a little dusty in the process.'

He gave Ambril a final pat on the back, sending up clouds of dust. 'Now then, the Director has an announcement to make.'

Ambril coughed and choked. 'Have I?'

'Yes, you have,' said Lon in steely tones.

Ambril cleared his throat, and began reciting, parrot-like. 'In honour of the special esteem in which we hold –'

'Get to the bit about the ceremony,' said Lon wearily.

'Ah yes, the ceremony.' Ambril drew himself up with a pathetic attempt at formal dignity. 'In the ceremony this afternoon, Lord Lon, son of the present Federator, will play the part of his illustrious ancestor, who, five hundred years ago, defeated the Mara and founded the Federation.' He paused, caught Lon's eye and stumbled on. 'In honour of this special occasion, the Great Crystal, the Great Mind's Eye, will for the first time be inserted in its rightful place –'

'No,' shouted Chela instinctively.

He fell silent, struck dumb by embarrassment.

'Oh, will that be difficult?' asked Lon, concerned. 'I know these last-minute changes of plan can sometimes cause problems.'

'Director,' said Chela desperately. 'It is expressly forbidden by your oath of office – '

'Superstition! Just foolish superstition.'

'It's all my fault, I'm afraid,' said Lon. 'It was all my idea.'

Chela stepped back, bowing his head. 'My Lord.'

Lon turned looked at his mother. 'Do you have any objection?'

Lady Tanha shook her head.

'Those are my instructions,' said Ambril with nervous determination. 'I will have them obeyed – to the letter!'

'Then fetch the Great Crystal, will you?' said Lon affably.

Ambril blenched. 'You mean – *now*, my Lord?'

'Yes. Why not now? We may as well have a look at it.'

Ambril stumbled out of the room.

Chela looked at the big metal key, on Ambril's desk. He began edging towards it.

'Well,' said Lon cheerfully. 'A drink while we're waiting, I think.' He smiled at Chela. 'Will you join us?'

By now Chela was leaning against Ambril's desk, his hands reaching out behind him. They touched the cold metal of the key. He straightened up. 'No thank you my Lord, I'm afraid I have duties.'

Chela backed towards the door.

'Of course, of course, very commendable,' said Lon. 'You mustn't neglect your duties.'

'Lon,' said Tanha protestingly, 'Please, *will* you tell me what is going on?'

Lon seemed to be in high spirits. 'With the greatest of pleasure, Mother.'

By now Chela was at the door. He bowed. 'Excuse

89

me, my Lord, my Lady – I'll send a servant to bring you wine.'

Chela slipped out of the room.

Lon rounded on Lady Tanha. 'What was on the table?'

Lady Tanha stared at him.

'He picked something up off the table. *What was it?*'

Chela hurried into the cell area, key in hand.

'Well done,' said the Doctor delightedly. 'Mind you, it's about time.'

'Be quiet,' said Chela impatiently. 'We must hurry, there is little time.' He unlocked the cell door.

'What made you change your mind?' asked the Doctor.

'Come *on*,' said Chela, and led the way from the room.

The bodyguards had been alerted, and now Lon was pacing up and down Ambril's study, waiting for news. 'It's no use making excuses for him, Mother,' Lon said impatiently. 'He's a traitor.'

'Are you sure? He seems such a pleasant young man.'

'He took the key, didn't he? That proves he's involved.'

Chela led them swiftly along the back corridors. 'We must get out of the building at once.'

'And back to the TARDIS,' said Nyssa. 'We'll be safe there.'

'*We* will, perhaps. What about Tegan?'

In Ambril's office, Lon was berating a guard. '*Why* haven't they been found yet? I want every entrance sealed. They must not escape.'

The guard hurried away

'Lon, I really do feel you're making too much of this,' protested Tanha.

'My dear Mother – do you really expect me to allow those who plot my death to go free?'

'Your death?'

'Isn't it obvious? This whole thing is a plot against my life – and those responsible must die!'

It would solve a lot of problems, thought Lon. An attack on the Federator or one of his family was the most dreadful crime imaginable. The death penalty would be automatic, and instant.

The three fugitives turned a corner and found themselves facing one of the bodyguards – a giant of a man in a terrifying mask-like helmet.

'Back the way we came!' ordered the Doctor.

They turned to run – but there was another bodyguard behind them.

'Oh no,' gasped Chela.

The Doctor raised his hands. 'All right, all right, we give in.'

Lon came around the corner. 'Give in? You talk as though you had a choice, Doctor.'

Lon clicked his fingers and the bodyguards drew their huge, curved swords.

Lon paused, savouring the moment. 'Kill them!' he said.

10

The Escape

The bodyguards raised their swords.

An imperious voice called, 'No!'

Lady Tanha was standing at the end of the corridor. 'You cannot do this Lon.'

There was new firmness in her voice, and for the moment Lon seemed reduced to a sulky child.

'Why not?' he demanded petulantly.

'It is preposterous to think that anyone is plotting against you. Least of all these people.'

The Doctor gave a sigh of relief. 'Your mother is quite right!'

'Naturally you deny everything,' said Lon morosely. 'That is only to be expected.'

'My only concern is for my companion Tegan – and to see that the Great Crystal is not misused.'

At this moment Ambril came along the corridor, clutching a small carved chest. 'Why should the Great Crystal concern you, Doctor?'

The Doctor indicated the sword still close to his throat. 'If I'm allowed to live long enough, I'll explain.'

In the market-place, preparations for the ceremony were well under way. Children looked on wide-eyed as the long painted cloth body of the ceremonial snake was unfurled by cat-faced demons in scarlet robes.

The Doctor looked in fascinated horror at the little carved chest in Ambril's hands. 'Use the real Great Crystal in the Ceremony? No, you mustn't do it.'

'And why not?' asked Tanha calmly.

'Mother – ' began Lon impatiently.

She waved him to silence. 'No! Let the man have his say, however preposterous.' She turned to the Doctor and said reasonably. 'Of course we can do this if we wish. The Director has agreed.' She glanced at Ambril. 'Haven't you?'

Ambril clasped the chest tighter. 'I have. The Great Crystal will be returned to its rightful place during the ceremony.'

The Doctor looked hard at Ambril. 'But why? *Why?*'

'Why what?' asked Lon idly.

'Why did you make this request? And why did the Director agree to it?'

'Why not?' said Tanha reasonably. 'Call it the indulging of a whim. It is, you might say, one of the few advantages of being a member of the Federator's family.'

Chela could keep silent no longer. 'But it is forbidden. It's forbidden by a tradition going back five hundred years.'

'Is that why you proposed to assassinate me?' accused Lon swiftly. 'For interfering with your precious traditions?'

'I thought we'd cleared that up,' said Lady Tanha wearily.

The Doctor looked at Lon in disbelief. 'Whoever said we wanted to assassinate you?'

Lon was forced to take refuge in bluster. 'I am not here to be questioned by you, Doctor.'

He tugged uneasily at the gauntlet that covered his

left arm, pulling it higher to make sure the snake design was concealed.

The Doctor noticed the gesture, and his eyes widened. 'No of course not. How foolish of me. Yes, I've been very stupid, haven't I?' He turned to Nyssa. 'You remember me telling you about the Mark of the Mara, Nyssa, on the Kinda world? I should have realised.'

Lon smiled. 'They'd never believe you, Doctor,' he said softly.

Lady Tanha looked from one to the other. 'What *are* you two talking about?'

The Doctor ignored her, addressing only Lon. 'Where is Tegan? What have you done with her?'

'Tegan?' said Tanha. 'Lon, who is this Tegan?'

'One of the Doctor's companions. Apparently he's managed to lose her.'

'Why is he asking you about her?'

'How should I know, Mother? That man is a complete and utter fool.'

The Doctor was still looking at Lon. 'You won't succeed in the end, you know. Evil never does.'

'Lon what does he mean?' asked Tanha uneasily. 'Evil? Who is evil?'

Lon gestured extravagantly. 'Oh I am, Mother, of course. Isn't it obvious? Your son is evil. Why else would they want to kill me? Don't you see?'

Any threat to her son made Lady Tanha both angry and defensive. Something about the Doctor's words to Lon had made her very uneasy. 'I most certainly do.' She waved to the guards. 'Take them away. Take them all away!'

Lon wanted to savour his triumph a little longer. 'Wait, Mother. On this day of all days I think we can afford to be a little generous. Let them see the Great

Crystal. Just once. Just for a moment. Don't you think so, Director?'

'My Lord,' protested Ambril.

Lon's voice hardened. '*Indulge me.*'

Lon signalled, and the guards brought the three prisoners closer to Ambril.

Lon raised his hand. 'That's far enough.' He nodded to Ambril. 'Right.'

'Must I, my Lord?'

'If you wouldn't mind,' said Lon in that same tone of silky command.

Ambril opened the little chest.

Every eye was fixed on the opening lid, eager for a glimpse of what was inside . . .

'Now,' shouted the Doctor. Nyssa grabbed one arm of the nearest bodyguard, the Doctor grabbed the other, and they yanked the man forwards with all their combined strength. Caught off guard and off balance the giant sprawled clumsily forwards, tripped over the Doctor's outstretched foot and fell, bringing down Lon and Lady Tanha with him. For a moment the room seemed full of a sprawling pile of bodies.

Chela made a move towards the Great Crystal, but the second bodyguard stepped in front of it, drawing his sword.

'No time for that, Chela,' yelled the Doctor. He grabbed his arm and pulled him towards the door. A moment later, all three fugitives were disappearing down the corridor.

The bodyguard hovered, torn between pursuing the fugitives and protecting his master and mistress while Ambril stood watching events in utter amazement.

Lon struggled to his feet. 'Well, don't just stand there, man, after them.'

'Me, my Lord?' said Ambril dubiously.

'Yes, you. And take that fool with you.' He nodded towards the second bodyguard. 'Leave the chest with me.'

'Very well, my Lord.' Reluctantly putting down the chest Ambril set off after the Doctor and the others, followed by the bodyguard.

Lon turned to the other bodyguard, who was lumbering to his feet. 'You – go with them. Off you go!'

Trying to straighten his armour and his face-mask, the bodyguard obeyed.

Lady Tanha was still sprawled out on the floor, though even in this position she managed to look dignified. 'Lon, will you please help me?'

Lon helped his mother to rise.

She brushed at her dress. 'Oughtn't we to call out the palace guards – or something?'

Lon went over to the chest. 'It doesn't matter. What can they do now? I have the Great Crystal!'

Exultantly, he took the crystal out of the box.

It wasn't particularly spectacular to look at, just a large dull stone, about the size of an orange.

Lon held it up exultantly. 'Now everything is prepared!'

The Doctor and his two friends headed for the crowded market area, busier than ever now with the preparation for the coming ceremony. They hid for a moment behind a stall, as a pursuing bodyguard went by.

As they hurried on their way Chela gasped. 'Where are we *going*, Doctor?'

'To find Tegan. She won't be far away, not with the ceremony so close.'

'We don't even know if she's still alive,' said Nyssa.

'Tegan won't die,' said the Doctor confidently. 'Not while the Mara still needs her. Not till the Mara inside her is free.'

'If Lon has been infected by the Mara, why hasn't he changed completely?'

'Same reason as with Tegan. He's got a very strong personality of his own, and there's still quite a lot of it left.'

'But he is – influenced?' asked Chela.

The Doctor nodded grimly. 'Very much so. Come on. We must find Tegan before it's too late.'

In the secret chamber, in the dim yellow light of the paper lanterns, the Mara had begun its Becoming. Eyes wide, face streaming with sweat, Dugdale stood watching as the great snake coiled about Tegan's arm.

Tegan, or rather the Mara, delighted in his terror. Fear was meat and drink to the Mara. 'Puzzling, isn't it Showman? How can it be happening? Can you believe your eyes? You have no choice! Dream on, Showman. I shall soon be triumphant.'

The snake coiled about Tegan's arm grew slowly larger.

Ambril staggered wearily back into his room, to find Lon still caressing the Great Crystal.

'Well?'

'No sign, my Lord. They seem to have got away.'

Lon received the news without particular interest. 'Do they?'

'I have issued the necessary instructions. A search is being organised.'

Lon stared into the Great Crystal. 'It doesn't matter. What can they do now?'

'As you say, my Lord.'

Lon nodded dismissively, but Ambril stood his ground.

Lon looked at him in mild surprise. 'Well?'

'I would only wish to remind you, my Lord . . . our – arrangement . . .'

Lon glanced quickly at Lady Tanha. 'Yes, yes. I have not forgotten.'

'You promised – immediately after the ceremony, my Lord.'

'Go *away*,' snarled Lon.

Ambril recoiled, bowed, and hurried from the room.

Lady Tanha turned fron the window, 'Lon, what is this arrangement? What did you promise him?'

'Nothing Mother. It really doesn't matter.'

'I know you, you're planning something. Is it to be a surprise?'

Lon smiled. 'Yes, Mother. A surprise.' He pushed back the chair and Tanha's eyes followed the movement.

Suddenly she leaned forward. 'Lon – what's wrong with your arm?'

The Doctor and his companions were resting in an abandoned archway behind the lines of market stalls. It was a quiet, gloomy place, and they welcomed the chance to get their breath back.

The Doctor peered out at the excited throng. The whole area was boiling with the excitement of the coming ceremony.

'It's all right,' gasped Chela. 'I think we've shaken them off!'

Suddenly a red-cloaked cat-faced apparition leaped at them out of the shadows, and they jumped back in alarm.

The creature darted forwards, tapped the Doctor on the shoulder and stood waiting expectantly, hand outstretched.

The Doctor and Nyssa peered apprehensively at it.

Chela was doubled up with laughter. 'I'm sorry, Doctor, you look so surprised.'

'Do you wonder? What is it?'

'You've been touched by an Attendant Demon,' said Chela solemnly. 'You must forfeit a coin. It's the custom, I'm afraid.'

'The custom?'

'On the day of the ceremony, the Attendant Demons seek out the unwary. Anyone they 'touch with evil' has to pay up or . . .'

'Or what?'

Chela grinned. 'Or get water tipped over them. It's part of the fun.'

The Demon gibbered, and reached threateningly for a bucket of water at its feet.

The Doctor smiled, recognising a Manussan version of trick or treat. 'I'm afraid I haven't got a coin.'

Chela reached into the pouch at his belt and handed the Demon a coin. 'Here you are. "May you never feel the Serpent's Tooth." '

The Demon picked up his bucket and moved off to look for fresh victims.

The Doctor said ruefully, 'I wish it was that easy to deal with the Mara!'

'Doctor, what are we going to do?' said Nyssa.

The Doctor turned to Chela. 'How long have we got – before the ceremony begins?'

'First the Great Snake has to be taken in procession through the street, before going up to the Cave of the

Snake . . .'

'*How* long?'

'A few hours, no more.'

The Doctor stood for a long moment lost in thought. 'I wonder. *Is* there still time?' He seemed to reach a decision. 'Come on, you two.'

'*Now* where are we going?' asked Chela.

'Change of plan,' said the Doctor, 'It's too late to look for Tegan. There's only one way to defeat the Mara now. We must find Dojjen.'

Chela stared at him. 'That's impossible, Doctor. Dojjen hasn't been seen for ten years or more. He could be anywhere.'

'I know. But we've got to find him. It's our only chance. If I'm to free Tegan and destroy the Mara, I *must* have Dojjen's help.'

11

Dojjen

Lady Tanha was gentle, but she could also be very persistent, and she was quite determined to examine Lon's arm.

'But if it's nothing, why won't you let me see?'

'I've told you,' said Lon sulkily. 'It's just a scratch.'

Tanha went on fussing. 'But it could become infected. How did it happen? Why didn't you tell me?'

'It's nothing I tell you. It was an accident.'

'What sort of accident? Show me Lon, I want to *see*.'

Lon turned on her, eyes blazing with anger. 'Mother, for the last time, *will you leave me alone?*'

He strode from the room, leaving Lady Tanha staring after him in dismay.

Excitement was rising high in the crowd by now. The Ceremonial Snake, a brightly painted affair attached to sticks held high by three men, was winding its way to and fro through the streets. Attendant Demons darted through the crowd, claiming their tributes of coins, splashing reluctant payers with water to howls of laughter from the onlookers. At the head of the Snake walked the Voice of the Mara, a tall red-robed apparition carrying a large red megaphone.

As the Snake weaved through the crowd, the Voice strode by its fiercely-grimacing head, bawling out the words of the ritual chant. 'Now the time has come for the Snake to claim his own. Who has the power to turn away his face? Which one of you has the strength to resist? Who can protect us now? Submit! Submit! Submit!'

The age-old terror of the Mara had been domesticated, turned into a comfortable, familiar ritual.

What no one realised as yet was that the Mara, the real Mara, was very close to its long-planned return.

The great snake coiled slowly round Tegan's arm. Its time was near.

The Doctor, Nyssa and Chela were clambering up the rockface above the Cave of the Snake. The Doctor seemed determined to reach the summit of the hill behind the caves. He leaned down and pulled first Nyssa and then Chela on to a ledge beside him, and they paused for a moment to rest.

From the city spread out below them, there drifted the buzz of the crowd and the faint tinkling of bells, the low drone of the megaphone-amplified voice.

'Come on,' said the Doctor. 'On we go.'

Chela didn't move. 'If you'd let me steal the Great Crystal when we had the chance this trek wouldn't be necessary.'

'You'd only have got yourself killed,' the Doctor pointed out. 'Besides, it's not as simple as that.'

'Why not?' asked Nyssa.

'We wouldn't be preventing the Mara's return, only postponing it. It would continue to exist as a mental force. No, this time we must destroy it completely.'

Nyssa gave him a despairing look. 'How?'

'I don't know.'

104

'But you think Dojjen will be able to tell us?'

'I can only hope so.'

'But I told you, Doctor,' protested Chela. 'Dojjen hasn't been seen for years. He could be anywhere. We don't even know if he's still alive.'

The Doctor held up the Snakedancer pendant. 'You're forgetting, we have this!'

'How will that help us find him?'

'It won't! But it will help him to find us. Now, trust me – and keep moving!'

They resumed their laborious climb.

Lady Tanha stood at the window, gazing out at the crowded city streets. Lon lay on the couch, brooding. It was some time since they had spoken.

There was a discreet tap on the door, and Ambril entered, a neatly-folded pile of garments in his hands. 'I have taken the liberty of bringing the clothes you must wear for the Ceremony, my Lord. The costume of the Sky Hero.'

Lon sprang to his feet. 'Oh good! Look, Mother.'

Tanha didn't move.

'It is an exact replica of the costume worn by your ancestor, the Founder of the Federation, who destroyed the Mara five hundred years ago.'

'How very appropriate.'

'I beg your pardon, my Lord?'

'Don't you think so, Mother?' asked Lon.

Tanha ignored him.

Lon took the costume from Ambril's arms. 'Well, I'm going to try it on. Mother, are you coming?'

Still there was no reply.

Lon shrugged. Tucking the costume under one arm, he scooped up the little chest containing the Great

Crystal with the other, and left the room.

There was a shallow depression at the very top of the hill, rimmed with huge boulders.

The Doctor regarded it with satisfaction.

'Right. Here will do very well.' The Doctor sat down, reached for the crystal around his neck, and held it up before his eyes.

Nyssa looked at him. 'What now?'

'Sympathetic resonance!'

'Sympathetic what?'

'Thought, directed at this crystal, should set up a resonance which is picked up and echoed by others.'

Chela sat cross-legged beside the Doctor. 'So?'

'Well, the Snakedancers wear these crystals, don't they?'

'I believe so.'

Nyssa sat down as well. 'Of course. The crystal will act like a radio wave, transmitting thoughts instead of words, establishing a mental link.'

'With Dojjen?' asked Chela.

The Doctor nodded. 'I very much hope so.'

'But will it work?'

'We can only try,' said the Doctor gently. He gazed deep into the crystal.

It began to glow . . .

Lady Tanha gazed broodingly out of the window. 'Do you have any children, Director Ambril?'

'No, my Lady. I have never married. My work . . .'

'You are very sensible,' said Tanha levelly. 'You have your — objects. An object lasts. You hold it in your hand and it belongs to you. Children can be very disappointing in that respect, don't you think so?'

'My Lady Tanha,' said Ambril unhappily. 'I really don't know.'

'I do . . .' She turned from the window, as Lon came back into the room.

'Mother? Look!'

Lon was resplendent in the costume of the Sky Hero. It consisted of a white toga with a starburst design on the breast, tied by a golden sash. On his head was an elaborate golden hat, crowned by a golden sunburst design, into which there was set a gleaming jewel.

He cut a handsome, heroic figure, and Tanha couldn't help being pleased. 'How splendid you are. Let me look at you.'

Lon went over to her. 'Am I forgiven?'

Tanha sighed. 'Of course. Aren't you always? You do look splendid, and it fits exactly. Don't you think so, Ambril?'

Ambril beamed with pride. 'A remarkable fit, my Lady. Truly remarkable.'

'Let me look at you,' said Lady Tanha again. 'I'm going to be so proud of you at the ceremony.'

Ambril produced a faded sheet of parchment. 'And here, my Lord, are the Responses.'

Exhausted with concentration, the Doctor closed his eyes. The glow of the crystal faded.

Nyssa looked around, as if expecting Dojjen to appear in a puff of smoke. 'Nothing!'

'He's not coming,' said Chela sadly.

The Doctor said, 'Be patient. Wait.'

They waited.

'Doctor?' said Chela.

'What?'

'If your theory about the Great Crystal is true, why

107

didn't Dojjen destroy it when he was still Director?'

'Good question, Chela. Nyssa asked me exactly the same thing.'

'Well?'

'I don't know. Perhaps it is as I said before – destroying the Great Crystal would have left the Mara in existence as a latent force. Maybe we *need* the Great Crystal to expose and destroy the Mara.'

Suddenly the crystal around the Doctor's neck began to glow again.

'Doctor!' whispered Nyssa. She pointed.

Silhouetted between two great rocks stood the figure of a tall white-haired old man, dressed in worn leather garments. He carried a staff, and there was a leather pouch at his belt. The crystal around his neck was glowing brightly, as if in answer to the Doctor's own.

The Doctor smiled in relief. 'Dojjen!'

Bells tinkled and cymbals clashed and horns blew as the Ceremonial Snake weaved its way towards the Cave. The megaphone voice boomed out: 'Abandon yourselves, and follow the path of the Snake! Follow the path! Who can resist the power of the Snake?'

Laughing and chattering excitedly, the crowd followed the Snake, forming a sort of informal procession, rushing all unknowing towards the horror that awaited them.

The Doctor and Dojjen sat facing each other, cross-legged, a few feet apart. Instinctively, Chela and Nyssa had moved away, watching from a respectful distance.

Slowly Dojjen reached into his pouch and produced a small green snake. It writhed in his hands, hissing angrily. Gripping it just behind the neck with his right hand, Dojjen slowly and deliberately moved the snake towards his own bare left forearm. As soon as it was in range, the snake darted its head forwards and bit him.

Dojjen sat quite motionless for a moment, then he held the still-writhing snake out to the Doctor. Slowly the Doctor pushed back his left sleeve. He reached out and took the snake in his right hand.

'No, Doctor,' called Nyssa. 'What are you doing? You mustn't let it bite you.'

The Doctor tightened his grip on the snake. 'I'm afraid there's no choice, not if we're to have any chance of saving Tegan and defeating the Mara.'

'But the venom could be deadly.'

'Yes, I know.'

Eyes fixed on Dojjen's, the Doctor brought the snake closer to his left wrist. He winced as he felt the sudden stab of its fangs.

By now the crowd was lining the steps that led up to the Cave of the Snake, cheering and clapping as the official party marched up the steps. Many of the crowd carried lanterns, others blew horns and threw streamers.

Magnificent in the Sky Hero costume, Lon marched at the head of the official procession. Behind him came Ambril and Lady Tanha, both suitably robed, and behind them, a small group of high officials. The crowd pressed forwards, cheering and waving, frantic to see, perhaps even to touch, the Sky Hero as he strode up the steps.

The Doctor could feel the deadly snake venom flooding through his veins. He could feel his senses slipping away. The only thing that was real, the only lifeline, was

Dojjen's voice. Strangely enough the voice did not come from Dojjen's lips. The voice spoke inside the Doctor's head.

'Look into my eyes,' said Dojjen. 'You have come this far. You must not give in to fear. Look.'

The Doctor seemed to be peering through a thickening mist. Dojjen's face bagan to quiver and dissolve, to spin and fade away.

'No!' said Dojjen's voice. 'Look at me!'

'Can't,' muttered the Doctor. 'It's the poison . . . the effect of the poison.'

The calm old voice said, 'Fear is the only poison.'

'Fear . . .' repeated the Doctor. 'Fear is the poison . . .'

'Ask your question.'

Somehow the Doctor managed to force the words from his lips. 'How . . . how can I . . . must save Tegan. My fault . . . my fault. How can the Mara . . . be destroyed? . . .' His voiced faded and he swayed dizzily.

'Steady your mind,' commanded the voice. 'Attach to nothing. Let go of your fear.'

The Doctor strove to obey. The spinning stopped, the mists cleared, and suddenly the Doctor was looking at Dojjen's face, blurred but perfectly recognisable. It was as if the rising tide of poison in his blood had halted, begun to recede.

The Doctor moistened his lips and whispered, 'What is the Snakedance?'

'This is. Here and now. The dance goes on. It is all the dance, everywhere and always. So you must find the still point. Only then can the Mara be defeated.'

The Doctor frowned in concentration. 'Still point? A point of safety? Somewhere in the Chamber?'

'No! The still point is within yourself, nowhere else.

110

To destroy the Mara you must find the still point . . .
point . . . point . . .'

The voice echoed and faded away, and the Doctor
was swallowed up in darkness.

In the Chamber of the Mara, chairs had been arranged
on a raised dais, set up beneath the carving of the Great
Snake. There were three larger, throne-like chairs in
front of the others. The little group of dignitaries stood
waiting in a murmuring group.

Ambril bustled in, carrying the chest that held the
Great Crystal, and went up to Lady Tanha. 'My Lady,
the Ceremonial Snake is approaching. We should take
our places.'

'Certainly,' said Lady Tanha graciously. She sat on
one of the three central chairs, and the dignitaries
moved to their places.

Ambril went up to Lon. My Lord, the Great Crystal—'

'I will tell you when,' said Lon tensely.

Ambril bowed. 'Very well, my Lord. We must take
our places.'

A roar of excitement went up from the crowd as the
great Ceremonial Snake writhed its way along the lane
and began climbing the steps to the Cave of the Snake.
Bells jangled, cymbals clashed, horns wailed, and once
again the red-robed Voice of the Mara bellowed the
ritual threats. 'Follow the path of the Great Snake!
Submit! Abandon yourself, and follow the path of the
Great Snake!'

As the Snake climbed the steps and disappeared into
the Cave, the excited crowd surged after it.

The Doctor heard a voice, calling to him in the

darkness.

'Doctor! Doctor wake up.' It was a voice that he recognised. It was Nyssa. He opened his eyes, and saw her worried face. The Doctor managed a smile . . . 'Hello, Nyssa . . .'

'Thank goodness! I thought for a moment . . .'

'Thought what?' The Doctor felt a faint soreness on his arm. He looked down at the two faint puncture marks.

The snake venom *had* been deadly, the Doctor was sure of that. Yet he felt perfectly well. The Snakedancers must have learned to neutralise the venom, the mind controlling the body completely. Somehow Dojjen had managed to transmit the power.

The Doctor smiled, and looked at Dojjen, who sat placidly, cross-legged, staring into space.

'I'm perfectly all right. I've – survived.'

'But how?'

'I don't know. Somehow Dojjen saw me through.'

Distant sounds of noise and excitement floated up to the hill top.

'We must hurry,' said Chela.

The Doctor jumped to his feet. 'Yes, of course. The ceremony.'

'But did you find out what you needed to know?' asked Nyssa.

'Yes, I think I did. We'll just have to see. Come on!'

The Doctor turned to hurry away, but Chela put a hand on his arm, and frowned warningly. The Doctor watched as Chela folded his arms across his chest and bowed low to Dojjen. Copying the gesture, the Doctor did the same. So did Nyssa.

With the Doctor leading the way, they scrambled down the steep path to the Cave of the Snake.

'Doctor, what are we going to *do*?' asked Chela.
'Stop the ceremony. I only hope we're not too late!'

12

The Becoming of the Mara

Ambril stood in the centre of the little group of dignitaries, Lady Tanha on his left, Lon on his right.

The Snake made its way into the Chamber of the Mara and came to a halt before the dais. There was a glass jewel in its jaws. The crowd pressed into the great Chamber, leaving a respectful space around the dais and the Ceremonial Snake. There was a hushed, expectant silence.

The Voice of the Mara stepped forward, bellowing through his megaphone, 'I speak here for the Mara! The Great Snake! The Father of Lies!'

There was a ceremonial rattling of castanets like the sound of angry rattlesnakes.

The Voice of the Mara bowed his head in mock grief. 'The thoughts of the Mara are black in my mind. Its words are bitter on my tongue. But I am too weak to resist.'

More clacking of castanets and a ritual moan of assent from the crowd.

'We are all too weak to resist!' boomed the Voice. 'The Mara has brought darkness to our hearts. It shows us death!'

More moans of grief and despair.

The Voice continued the ritual chant. 'Who will challenge the Mara? Who will pluck the Great Crystal of knowledge from between the Mara's jaws and set us free?'

(Lady Tanha leaned over and whispered, 'Lon?' Ambril shook his head. 'Not yet, my Lady.')

'For the second time I ask,' bellowed the Voice. 'Who will challenge the Mara?'

Another rattling of castanets.

'For the third and final time!'

Ambril tapped Lon on the shoulder.

Lon rose to his feet. 'I will!'

There was wild applause from the spectators.

'Bring the Stranger forward,' commanded the Voice.

Lon strode from the dais, an impressive figure in his white-and-gold toga, and the helmet with its great jewelled sunburst. Two red-robed cat-faced Attendant Demons took him by the arms and pulled him to stand before the Ceremonial Snake.

'You dare to challenge the Power of the Mara?' boomed the Voice.

'I do.'

'And in whose name do you do so?'

'In the Federation's name, and in my own.'

Yet another burst of applause.

'First let the Stranger prove his worthiness,' commanded the Voice. 'Prepare him for the Test!'

Lon drew the gauntlet from one arm – the unmarked one – and the Demons pushed back his sleeve. He held out his arm.

'Stranger, are you ready to face the triple temptation?'

'I am ready.'

'The first temptation is Fear. I offer you fear, in a handful of dust.'

An Attendant Demon came forward, bearing a

human skull filled with dust. It poured the dust in a fine stream over Lon's outstretched hand.

Lon made the ritual response in which Ambril had coached him before the Ceremony. 'I do not fear. I spread my fingers and the dust trickles away.' Lon suited the action to the words. 'I know that whilst I live, my hand is clean, my eyes are bright. That is enough.'

There was more applause.

'I claim the right to strike the first blow.'

'Stranger, you have earned it.'

Lon struck the Ceremonial Snake a token blow on its papier-mâché head.

The Doctor and his two companions heard the chanting and the applause as they climbed down the last few feet of the path.

Chela jumped down. The Doctor followed, and turned to Nyssa. 'Come on, jump!'

He reached out and took her arm, half-lifting her down.

'Thank you,' said Nyssa stiffly. 'But it wasn't necessary.'

They hurried into the Cave.

The Voice boomed, 'Are you ready for the second temptation?'

'I am ready.'

The second temptation is to Despair. I offer you despair in a withered branch.'

A Demon thrust a withered branch into Lon's hand.

'I do not despair. I turn my hand, the branch drops to the ground.' Lon let the branch fall. 'I know the sap will rise again, the roots will sprout. That is enough.'

The onlookers clapped again.

Lon said, 'I claim the right to strike the second blow.'

'Stranger, you have earned it.'

Lon gave the Ceremonial Snake a second token blow.

The Doctor and his two companions heard the applause as they hurried down the access tunnel.

'The ceremony must have started,' said Chela.

The Doctor nodded. 'Just so long as it hasn't finished!'

'Doctor, look!' Nyssa pointed down the tunnel.

A massive figure was striding purposefully towards them. It was one of the Federation bodyguards. It was obvious that he had recognised them as fugitives.

'The third and final temptation is to succumb to Greed. Stranger, you must look into the Crystal.' The voice indicated the Crystal – a lump of coloured glass – in the mouth of the Ceremonial Snake. 'Look into the Crystal without greed for knowledge. I offer you greed, in the hidden depths.'

By now Lon was weary of the Ceremony. Shaking off the Demons he reached out to take the fake crystal. There was a murmur from the onlookers, and Ambril hurried forward. 'No, my Lord, you must not touch it yet.'

There was a whole complicated ritual of questions and answers still to be gone through.

Lon pushed Ambril aside. '*Why* mustn't I touch it?'

The Voice attempted to resume the ritual. 'Beware, Stranger. The Crystal of Knowledge has hidden depths.'

'What do you mean? Hidden depths! Show them to me. It's just a fake. Your whole Ceremony is a fake. Look!' Lon reached up and snatched the chunk of glass

118

from the Snake's jaws.

There were more horrified mutterings from the crowd. The sacred ritual, unchanged for five hundred years, was being profaned.

Lon held the mock crystal high. 'It's nothing. It's just glass.' He dashed it to the ground and it shattered on the rocky floor.

The Doctor and Nyssa separated. The guard moved closer.

As he drew his sword to strike, the Doctor sprang forwards, grabbing the man's arm and thrusting the sword aside.

Nyssa ran to help him.

Unfortunately the bodyguard was more than a match for both of them. The Doctor realised it would only be a matter of moments before he broke free. And if he got a chance to use that sword . . .

Suddenly Chela leaped out of the shadows and delivered a chopping blow at the bulging muscle at the back of the man's neck. The guard slumped to the ground.

The Doctor gave Chela a reproving look. 'You left that a bit late! Come on, hurry!'

They ran towards the Chamber of the Mara.

'This whole Ceremony is a fake,' shouted Lon. 'A childish farce, created by a civilisation that has gone soft. Today I bring real knowledge and real power.' Lon crossed over to Ambril, reaching out for the chest that held the real Great Crystal. 'Give it to me.'

'My Lord, no . . .'

'Give me the Great Crystal.'

Lady Tanha put her hand on the chest. 'Lon, please!

What's wrong with you?'

'Mother, let go!' snarled Lon. He stripped off his other gauntlet, revealing the Mara snake sign on his arm.

Lady Tanha stared at it appalled. 'Lon! What is that?'

Thrusting her aside, Lon snatched the chest, opened it, and took out the Great Crystal – the real one. He turned, strode over to the carving of the Great Snake, and raised his voice commandingly. 'Now, listen to me, all of you. I hold in my hands the Great Crystal. The Great Crystal that was removed from the socket here by my ancestor, when the Mara was banished to the Dark Places of the Inside. Now, after five hundred years the Mara has returned. It is fitting that I should be the one to restore the Great Crystal to its rightful place.'

Lon reached out and pressed the snake design on his arm against a section of the wall. The door to the secret chamber swung open – and Tegan appeared.

There was a gasp of terror from the crowd. Around Tegan's arm was coiled an enormous, writhing snake.

Lon held up the Crystal to the socket and Tegan hissed, 'Go on. Do it now!'

He was about to thrust the Great Crystal into the socket when the Doctor's voice rang out. 'No. No, you mustn't.'

But he was too late.

Lon reached up and thrust the Crystal into place. For a moment time seemed frozen. Then there came a low roaring, hissing sound, that filled the ears and numbed the mind. Energy lines flared brightly in the wall, carrying a surge of power to Tegan, and the Snake that encased her arm. People were screaming, falling to the ground, covering their ears, but nothing could shut out

120

that terrible sound.

Tegan emerged from the doorway, Dugdale stumbling behind her. She held out her arm, and the snake dropped to the ground. It began to grow. The eyes of the crowd were riveted on the living Snake, hypnotised by its evil presence. The Doctor saw that even Chela and Nyssa were in its grip.

He raised his voice. 'No,' he shouted. 'Don't look. You must not look. The Mara is feeding off the fear and the panic. It *needs* your fear, your belief. You must *not* believe what you are seeing. The Great Crystal is absorbing the belief and creating the Mara. Don't look! Reach into yourself and find the still point!'

It was no use.

Chela, Nyssa, the dignitaries, the spectators — nobody was in a state to heed the Doctor's words. It is doubtful if they were even heard.

The Snake was colossal now, towering over the crowd.

Tegan gazed up at it. To the Doctor's horror she seemed to blur into it, to be absorbed, swallowed, so that *her* face looked out from between the slavering jaws. Everyone in the great cave was under the sway of the Mara. Everyone believed in its reality, its invincible power. Everyone but the Doctor.

The colossal Snake pulsed and blurred for a moment. Tegan spoke in the Mara voice, from out of the jaws of the snake. '*What is happening? Who dares to interrupt the Becoming? Who does not believe?*'

The Doctor moved slowly forward, looking not at the Mara but at the crystal around his neck.

'*Submit,*' roared the Mara. '*All minds must submit. Look at me. You must look at me. You cannot resist, it is impossible.*'

Still staring into the glowing crystal, the Doctor

advanced.

'*Stop him,*' screamed the Mara. '*He must be destroyed!*'

Zombie-like, Lon and Dugdale moved to intercept the Doctor.

Suddenly Tegan spoke in her own, natural voice. 'Doctor, help me,' she pleaded. 'What's happening to me? Please, *look* at me Doctor! I need your help.'

For a moment the Doctor was deceived. Then he realised this wasn't the real Tegan, but a trick of the Mara, the Father of Lies.

The Doctor felt as if invisible hands were trying to twist his head to force him to look at Tegan, but he gazed steadfastly into the crystal. 'No!' he shouted. 'I will not submit!'

The deep pulsing roar swelled to unbearable force and the Doctor could feel the anger of the Mara battering against his mind. For a moment he faltered, then the wise old face of Dojjen appeared in the crystal. His eyes opened and he gazed placidly at the Doctor.

'The still point,' said the voice in the Doctor's head. 'Find the still point.'

'*No!*' roared the Mara. '*Destroy that crystal. It will prevent my Becoming!*'

Dugdale lumbered forward and grabbed at the crystal around the Doctor's throat – but the moment he touched it, a surge of energy threw him across the cave.

Lon flung himself upon the Doctor.

The Doctor dodged, ran to the carving of the Great Snake, and reached up to take the Great Crystal from its socket. He couldn't move it.

The Great Crystal seemed fixed in place as if magnetised by the energy-flow.

The Doctor tugged in vain.

Lon flung himself upon the Doctor's back, trying to

drag him away.

The Doctor tightened his grip on the Great Crystal — and their combined weights pulled it free.

As it came out of the socket, the Mara serpent gave one last terrible scream.

The colossal Snake slumped to the floor. Instantly it began to decay, as if time had been speeded up.

The disintegrating Snake writhed and hissed and steamed, body-fluids spurting. In a matter of seconds, it was a rotting mass of carrion.

On the hill above the Cave of the Snake, Dojjen rose from his sitting position, and moved slowly away.

His work was done.

The Doctor found Tegan, a blessedly normal Tegan, sitting hunched on the edge of the dais. She was white-faced and trembling but her eyes were clear, and the mark of the Mara was gone from her arm. The Doctor went and sat beside her.

She looked up at him and sobbed, 'It was awful. Awful!'

The Doctor put a comforting arm around her shoulders. 'It's all right now, Tegan. It's all over.'

'You don't understand, Doctor. The feelings of hate and rage . . . It was terrible. I wanted to destroy everything.'

Awkwardly the Doctor patted her shoulder. 'I know. But you're free of it now.'

'Has it really gone — forever?'

The Doctor looked at the pile of putrefying snake flesh in the centre of the cave. 'Yes. The Mara has been destroyed.'

He looked round the cave. People everywhere were slowly recovering, staring wildly at each other, too astonished to speak. The Doctor saw Ambril picking up the Great Crystal, and restoring it lovingly to the wooden chest. He saw Lon still dazed, with Lady Tanha cradling his head in her lap. Chela was rubbing his eyes, staring around him in astonishment. They could all take up their lives again, thought the Doctor. Manussa was free at last of the menace of Mara.

He felt too tired for explanations and thanks and congratulations. Best to slip away now. Let the Manussans make what sense they could of their terrifying escape. They could invent another ceremony.

The Doctor took Tegan by the arm, collected a still-dazed Nyssa, and led them out of the Cave, down the steps, and through the deserted market quarter towards the TARDIS.

Despite his exhaustion the Doctor felt strangely at peace.

In his mind's eye, he could see Dojjen striding away into the hills. The old man turned and waved in farewell.

DOCTOR WHO

0426114558	TERRANCE DICKS **Doctor Who and The Abominable Snowmen**	**£1.35**
0426200373	**Doctor Who and The Android Invasion**	**£1.25**
0426201086	**Doctor Who and The Androids of Tara**	**£1.25**
0426116313	IAN MARTER **Doctor Who and The Ark in Space**	**£1.25**
0426201043	TERRANCE DICKS **Doctor Who and The Armageddon Factor**	**£1.25**
0426112954	**Doctor Who and The Auton Invasion**	**£1.50**
0426116747	**Doctor Who and The Brain of Morbius**	**£1.35**
0426110250	**Doctor Who and The Carnival of Monsters**	**£1.25**
042611471X	MALCOLM HULKE **Doctor Who and The Cave Monsters**	**£1.50**
0426117034	TERRANCE DICKS **Doctor Who and The Claws of Axos**	**£1.35**
042620123X	DAVID FISHER **Doctor Who and The Creature from the Pit**	**£1.25**
0426113160	DAVID WHITAKER **Doctor Who and The Crusaders**	**£1.50**
0426200616	BRIAN HAYLES **Doctor Who and The Curse of Peladon**	**£1.50**
0426114639	GERRY DAVIS **Doctor Who and The Cybermen**	**£1.50**
0426113322	BARRY LETTS **Doctor Who and The Daemons**	**£1.50**

Prices are subject to alteration

DOCTOR WHO

0426101103	DAVID WHITAKER **Doctor Who and The Daleks**	**£1.50**
042611244X	TERRANCE DICKS **Doctor Who and The Dalek Invasion of Earth**	**£1.25**
0426103807	**Doctor Who and The Day of the Daleks**	**£1.35**
042620042X	**Doctor Who – Death to the Daleks**	**£1.35**
0426119657	**Doctor Who and The Deadly Assassin**	**£1.25**
0426200969	**Doctor Who and The Destiny of the Daleks**	**£1.35**
0426108744	MALCOLM HULKE **Doctor Who and The Dinosaur Invasion**	**£1.35**
0426103726	**Doctor Who and The Doomsday Weapon**	**£1.35**
0426201464	IAN MARTER **Doctor Who and The Enemy of the World**	**£1.25**
0426200063	TERRANCE DICKS **Doctor Who and The Face of Evil**	**£1.25**
0426201507	ANDREW SMITH **Doctor Who – Full Circle**	**£1.35**
0426112601	TERRANCE DICKS **Doctor Who and The Genesis of the Daleks**	**£1.35**
0426112792	**Doctor Who and The Giant Robot**	**£1.25**
0426115430	MALCOLM HULKE **Doctor Who and The Green Death**	**£1.35**

Prices are subject to alteration

DOCTOR WHO

	TERRANCE DICKS **Doctor Who and The**	
0426200330	**Hand of Fear**	£1.25
	Doctor Who and The	
0426201310	**Horns of Nimon**	£1.25
	Doctor Who and The	
0426200098	**Horror of Fang Rock**	£1.25
	BRIAN HAYLES **Doctor Who and The**	
0426108663	**Ice Warriors**	£1.35
	Doctor Who and The	
0426200772	**Image of the Fendahl**	£1.25
	TERRANCE DICKS **Doctor Who and The**	
0426200934	**Invasion of Time**	£1.35
	Doctor Who and The	
0426200543	**Invisible Enemy**	£1.25
	Doctor Who and The	
0426201485	**Keeper of Traken**	£1.35
	PHILIP HINCHCLIFFE **Doctor Who and The**	
0426201256	**Keys of Marinus**	£1.35
	DAVID FISHER **Doctor Who and The**	
0426201477	**Leisure Hive**	£1.25
	TERRANCE DICKS **Doctor Who and The**	
0426110412	**Loch Ness Monster**	£1.25
	CHRISTOPHER H BIDMEAD	
0426201493	**Doctor Who – Logopolis**	£1.25
	PHILIP HINCHCLIFFE **Doctor Who and The**	
0426118936	**Masque of Mandragora**	£1.25
	TERRANCE DICKS **Doctor Who and The**	
0426201329	**Monster of Peladon**	£1.25

Prices are subject to alteration

STAR Books are obtainable from many booksellers and newsagents. If you have any difficulty please send purchase price plus postage on the scale below to:-

Star Cash Sales
P.O. Box 11
Falmouth
Cornwall
OR
Star Book Service,
G.P.O. Box 29,
Douglas,
Isle of Man,
British Isles.

While every effort is made to keep prices low, it is sometimes necessary to increase prices at short notice. Star Books reserve the right to show new retail prices on covers which may differ from those advertised in the text or elsewhere.

Postage and Packing Rate
UK: 45p for the first book, 20p for the second book and 14p for each additional book ordered to a maximum charge of £1.63. BFPO and EIRE: 45p for the first book, 20p for the second book, 14p per copy for the next 7 books thereafter 8p per book. Overseas: 75p for the first book and 21p per copy for each additional book.